JAMES BOWIE (Boo-wie)

AND HIS FAMOUS KNIFE

The adventure packed story of the inventor of the famous Bowie knife, who helped create an empire in the exciting West. He knew the fierce Indians who roamed the Texas plains in 1830 and rode fearlessly among them on a mission aimed at healing the growing quarrel between Mexico and the United States. Tensions exploded in the historic battle of the Alamo, where Bowie and his men died defending their nation.

Books by Shannon Garst

AMELIA EARHART: *Heroine of the Skies*
ANNIE OAKLEY
BIG FOOT WALLACE OF THE TEXAS RANGERS
BROKEN-HAND FITZPATRICK: *Greatest of Mountain Men*
BUFFALO BILL
CHIEF JOSEPH OF THE NEZ PERCES
COWBOY-ARTIST: *Charles M. Russell*
CUSTER: *Fighter of the Plains*
FRONTIER HERO: *Simon Kenton*
JACK LONDON: *Magnet for Adventure*
JAMES BOWIE AND HIS FAMOUS KNIFE
KIT CARSON: TRAIL BLAZER AND SCOUT
SITTING BULL: *Champion of His People*
THREE CONQUISTADORS: *Cortez, Coronado, Pizarro*
WILL ROGERS: *Immortal Cowboy*

with Warren Garst

ERNEST THOMPSON SETON: *Naturalist*
WILD BILL HICKOK

JAMES BOWIE

AND HIS FAMOUS KNIFE

BY

SHANNON GARST

LIBRARY EDITION

RESPONSIVE ENVIRONMENTS CORP.
ENGLEWOOD CLIFFS, N.J. 07632

This edition is published by arrangement with
Julian Messner, a Division of Simon & Schuster, Inc.

Printed in the United States of America
Library of Congress Catalog Card No. 55-6927

Dedicated to the

HEROES OF THE ALAMO

CONTENTS

Chapter One

A THRILLING RIDE

Jim stepped light footed as a deer through the tangled underbrush along the edge of the beautiful Bayou Teche. Sunlight seeping through the tangled bearded moss which draped the live oaks glistened on his tousled red hair. His blue eyes were alert, for danger lurked in this swampy, jungle country.

He was dressed in a suit of soft buckskin with long fringes, which served not only as decoration but could be cut off and used for numerous tying or mending jobs. In one hand he carried a cloth sack. His other hand, by force of habit, rested on the knife he always wore in a sheath at his belt.

He had left Rezin, his older brother, back a ways sitting on the edge of the bayou fishing. Fishing was not an exciting enough sport for Jim's restless spirit. So he had wandered along the bayou catching turtles sunning themselves on the rocks. Mammy Lou could use them for soup or gumbo.

But the turtles were too easy to catch to suit him, so he took the lariat from his belt. Like his knife, this was standard equipment wherever he went. Constant practice had made him unusually adept in the throwing of both the lasso and the knife.

In this wild Teche country a man's life depended upon these skills. Jim was a good marksman, too. His father had seen to it that his sons could handle a rifle, but guns were cumbersome and ammunition scarce and expensive, so the boys' preference was for a rope or a knife.

Jim shook out his loop and sent it spinning to where an old granddaddy turtle basked upon a stump. His lasso found its mark, but the turtle slipped through the noose and splashed into the water.

"Guess they aren't the right shape for roping." Jim spoke aloud and chuckled at the eerie, hollow sound of his voice in this lonely swampland.

He stopped when he came to a river, sluggish and choked with water hyacinths.

"Why don't we build a canoe?" He again spoke aloud as he often did on his lonely wanderings. His imagination raced ahead to the wonderful exploring jaunts he and Rezin could have paddling up the numerous lagoons and creeks which fed the Bayou Teche. John might come along sometimes, too, although he was seven years older than Jim and was not so adventurous as his two younger brothers. Surely in the back country would be Cajun villages and farther on camps of the half-wild Caddo Indians.

The more he thought about it, the more enthusiastic he became about having a pirogue—a dugout canoe. They could make it from a cypress log, as the Indians did, burning out the inside. He and Rezin had ranged far on horseback, but they could not ride in the swampy ground along the bayous. In a pirogue they could explore parts of the country beyond their reach.

A queer-looking log half covered by the water hyacinths caught Jim's eye. Almost automatically his rope began to twirl. It snaked out and fell neatly about the point of the log. As he tightened the noose, the "log" thrashed and churned the water. He had roped an alligator! He dug his heels into the soft ground and pulled hard on the rope, choking the great creature into submission. Then with a whoop Jim splashed through the water. Throwing himself upon the back of the gator, he loosened the rope a trifle to give the creature enough air to enable it to give him an interesting ride.

"Jim! Jim!" It was Rezin's voice shrill with alarm. "What on earth are you doing?"

"Yipee!" Jim shouted. A wide grin split his handsome face. "I've tamed me a gator. He's going to take me swamp riding."

"You crazy loon!" Rezin shouted. "Get off before he flops over and takes off an arm or leg."

The idea sobered Jim slightly. Anyway, by this time the thrill was lessening. He had ridden a gator—a feat that would certainly make John sit up and take notice.

He gave his rope a jerk to tighten it, leaped off and splashed to shore as fast as his long legs would take him. Shaking his rope from the monster he made it into a neat coil which he tucked into his belt. As soon as it was free the alligator rolled over on its back.

"See!" Rezin said, his eyes still large with alarm. "If he'd rolled with you on him, you wouldn't have had a chance. Haven't you any sense?"

"Sure." Jim grinned. "Sense enough to keep the rope so tight he couldn't bite me."

Rezin shook his head. "It's the craziest thing I ever heard of."

"It's fun," Jim insisted. "Try it sometime."

Jim strutted a bit as he and Rezin strode along the trail toward home. He was glad that he had tried this alligator riding stunt first. "Those wild Bowie boys" their neighboring Acadian and Spanish neighbors called them. There was always good-natured rivalry between the brothers in doing dangerous and exciting things and in excelling in markmanship and roping.

"We're going to make us a pirogue," Jim announced as they swung along in step with each other.

"Zat so?"

"Yeh. I've got a hankering to explore the back country of the Cajuns and the Caddo."

"There are plenty of Acadians all around us," his brother pointed out. "And Caddo come in to Opelousas to trade every Saturday."

"Yes. But those are tame ones. I want to see how they live in their villages. I hear tell that some of the Cajuns in the back country have never come near a town. And I've never seen an Indian village."

"It might be just as well to stay away from them," Rezin said sensibly. "And I suppose the backwoods Cajuns are just like the backwoods Tennesseans, where we used to live."

"But I never saw them," Jim said. "We left Tennessee before I was knee high to a grasshopper."

"That's right. You weren't born till the spring of '96. What a noise you made! And you've kept it up ever since."

Jim chuckled. "You were only two when I was born. You can't remember. But Mom says the reason we left Tennessee and moved to Kentucky was because I yelled so loud it drew the Indians to our plantation. But I think the reason we moved from Kentucky to Georgia, then here to Louisiana, is because Dad likes moving. I hope we stay here, though. I like it!"

They trudged in silence for a time. Jim looked around in deep content at the gigantic Spanish moss-bearded live oaks, at the great cypress spraddled in the lagoons.

It was a peaceful yet mysterious country which cast a spell upon the imagination. Ever since the first day they arrived Jim had felt quite at home in this tranquil land of the Acadians.

His father, the elder Rezin Pleasant Bowie, had brought along about a dozen slaves from his Tennessee plantation. He had built a rambling farmhouse and began raising sugar cane in the rich bottom lands near Opelousas—the town named after the Opelousas Indians.

Reaching home, Rezin lost no time in telling about Jim's latest exploit to the Bowie children gathered in the shade of the magnolia. David and Stephen, the younger brothers, frowned in envy, obviously wishing they were old enough to join in such wild activities. Sarah and Mary squealed over such daring and John, the steady, sober one of the three older boys, shook his head and said, "Such show off doings are just plain silly."

"But I wasn't showing off." Quick anger blazed in Jim's blue eyes. "There wasn't anyone there to see—at first. Eat those words, John Bowie, or I'll ram 'em down your throat."

"Yes?" John's tone was contemptuous, which only added fuel to Jim's flaring anger. He leaped at John with pounding knuckles.

One blow from John's great fist sent the lighter boy reeling. Seeing his younger brother getting the worst of it, Rezin loyally jumped into the battle to help—and from then on it was so mixed up no one could tell who was who.

A figure in wide ruffled skirts raced from the house. "Boys! Stop it. Stop it this instant I say."

Slowly the three brothers straightened up and wiped their bloody noses.

"For shame!" the little woman cried. "How many times do I have to tell you that I will not tolerate fighting among you? I'm trying to teach you to behave like gentlemen."

"I'm sorry, Mom." The three boys spoke as one.

"Now shake hands and apologize to each other." Her voice was low, but it held the note of authority which commanded instant obedience. They turned and gripped hands and grinned as they sheepishly said a brief, "Sorry!"

"Jimmy rode a gator, Mom," Stevie shrilled.

"Jimmy what?" Mrs. Bowie turned with a shocked expression on her delicate features.

"Rode a gator," the boy repeated.

"Your father shall hear of this," she threatened, as she whisked into the house.

The boys looked at each other apprehensively as they washed for supper at the long bench outside the kitchen. Soberly they filed inside to wait until Mammy Lou had the meal ready to serve. Mrs. Bowie was back at the spinning wheel where she spent most of her time. With six children to clothe the pleasant whirr of the wheel could be heard at any time of day, and often it lulled the boys to sleep at night.

When Mr. Bowie came in from the fields, the evening meal was served.

"Jimmy rode an alligator today," his wife said. "I'd thank you, Rezin, to put a stop once and for all to such foolhardiness."

He turned his dark gaze on Jim. "Is that right, son?"

Jim nodded. "Yes, suh."

"I admire bravery," his father said slowly. "But you're mighty reckless, seems to me."

"It was fun." Jim knew that this was a pretty feeble excuse, but he could think of nothing better.

"I'm not going to forbid you to do it again," his father said. "I know that forbidden fruit always tastes sweetest. I don't want to tempt you to disobey me. But to survive on the frontier, you need good old common horse sense. I ask you to try to cultivate it."

"Yes, suh," Jim said meekly. For a few moments they were all silent, then Jim burst into an explosive snicker.

"What are you laughing at?" his mother demanded.

"I was thinking of the time back in Tennessee when you got Pa out of jail by pointing a pistol at the sheriff."

Everyone burst into laughter. The story was an old one often told but gained savor by each repetition. Mr. Bowie had been bothered by a squatter who settled on a choice plot of his land and who refused to move until the elder Rezin backed up his threats with a rifle load of bird shot. He was arrested. Whereupon Elvira, his wife, had one of the slaves drive her to the jail where she informed the sheriff that she had come to visit her husband. Shortly man and wife confronted the officer, each armed with a pistol which the little woman had concealed under her full skirts.

"You haven't any business holding my husband for defending his rights," she told the sheriff. "He's needed at home and I'm taking him."

"I was about to let him go," the man said meekly.

Mr. Bowie laughed as heartily as his children over this story. "Jim's right, Elvie," he chuckled. "Shows where he gets his reckless nature."

"I wonder where he gets his wanderlust—his hankering to be always on the move exploring new places," she remarked, with a toss of her blonde head.

Chapter Two

HOW TO TRAP A BEAR

Jim's bare feet hit the rough plank floor with a smack. The narrow slit of sunlight entering at the edge of the oiled hide at the window had wakened him. Always the first one up, he never lost much time in rousing his brothers. The boys slept in the attic on bunks built against the walls, their mattresses and pillows stuffed with Spanish moss.

Jim liked to get up early in order to practice roping or throwing the knife at some tree stump or having a horse race with Rezin and John.

There was continuous excitement and adventure to be found in the Louisiana bayou country—possum hunting with hound dogs, fishing, turtle catching, hunting wild turkeys, geese, ducks, partridges and deer. Besides the wealth of wild game there were persimmons, grapes, wild figs and muscadines to eat. This was the life for a red-blooded, adventure-loving boy! Yet there were less pleasant sides to it, for Mrs. Bowie was determined that her lively brood should be as well educated as she herself.

Mr. Bowie had been too busy either fighting Indians or in the Revolutionary War to get much education. Nevertheless he was a highly intelligent man and commanded the respect both of his children and the community. His spelling, though, showed lack of schooling. His own name bore witness to this. He has been christened Reason Pleasant Bowie, but he always signed his first name as it sounded—Rezin. And his son and namesake used the same spelling.

After a rousing race to the edge of the bayou John, Rezin and Jim handed their horses over to Jeb, one of the slave boys. They washed up hastily and went in to devour hoecakes, hominy grits, corn pone and roast bass, washing it down with steaming chicory from gourd cups. When the meal was over Mammy Lou removed the dishes but the children, with the exception of the toddlers, remained in their places.

Jim sighed deeply as he brought the schoolbooks, tossing them on the table with a lack of grace and willingness which brought a frown of disapproval from his mother.

"Sorry, Mom. They slipped." He flashed his wide grin which he had already learned could quite disarm not only cross parents but other people, too.

He slid into his place on the long bench and picked up the arithmetic book. There was an hour of silent study, the children taking turns with the grammar, the Latin primer, the Bible, *Pilgrim's Progress* and a battered copy of Shakespeare's plays. During this time Elvira Bowie bustled about her household duties. Then for another hour she listened to recitations.

Jim resented this time of inaction, but he had learned the uselessness of shirking his lessons; he would only have to sit in the house longer and study, while the others were whooping outside. So he had learned to apply his fine intelligence to the task at hand, and through concentration he learned quickly.

After lessons the girls were set to spinning or carding wool or working on their samplers. The older boys went to help their father. Although there were slaves to do the labor, Mr. Bowie was determined that his sons should know how to run a plantation. So they helped with the cane, the cotton, the tobacco, and the mule-drawn sugar presses, or worked in the sawmill in which Mr. Bowie had an interest. In the afternoons they were free to do as they pleased.

Their "parish"—as a Louisiana county is called—of St. Landry was populated mainly by French-and Spanish-speaking people. The Bowie boys quickly learned to speak these languages.

The afternoons were never long enough for all the exciting things they wanted to do. Now Rezin and Jim were building a pirogue, but before they got it finished a new project had to be undertaken. Bears were raiding the sugar cane and their father told the boys to take rifles and lie in wait for the intruders.

"We could wait for days," Jim cried impatiently, "and never catch them. I've a better plan than that. John and Rezin, you can come and help me this afternoon—that is, if Pa'll let me borrow a mule and some long spikes."

"Anything you like," his father agreed. "Just so you get rid of those bears."

"Follow me!" Jim cried as he mounted his favorite horse—Fleetfoot.

His brothers were also mounted and armed with axes. Jim led a big gray mule called Molasses, because he was so slow. Now, however, the mule sensed the excitement in the air and trotted along with the horses.

They followed Jim into the woods to a bee tree, which was hollow about halfway up. The boys dismounted and built a brush fire beneath the tree. Dipping Spanish moss from the live oaks into the near-by stream, they made a smudge which nearly choked them as well as the bees.

When the bees had been smoked from their home the boys set to work with their axes and brought down the tree with its precious store of honey. Jim chained the log to the mule and led the way to the edge of the sugar cane field where tracks showed that the bears had been entering.

He and his brothers drove spikes into the log on a slant. Then Jim spread a generous gob of honey on a flat leaf and thrust it as far back into the log as he could reach.

"Now," he said, waving his hand with a flourish, "please step into my parlor, Mr. Bear. A feast is waiting."

"You're clever," John said. "I never would have thought of such a trap. The bears will be able to get his head in easily when he goes after the honey. But he won't be able to draw it out because the spikes are slanted inward."

"Just a nice collar for Bruin." Jim chuckled, well pleased with himself.

Next morning the three boys rode out to look at their trap. Sure enough, a bear was snorting and growling his disapproval of the "collar" he had acquired.

"Dibs on the hide," Jim said as John raised his rifle to shoot the marauding beast. "That will be one less bear to raid our sugar field."

After several bears were caught in this fashion the raiding stopped.

Rezin and Jim went back to finishing their pirogue. John spent most of his time working with their father. He felt himself too old for many of the activities of his younger brothers. Between Rezin and Jim, however, there was an extraordinarily strong bond. They liked the same things and could laugh and chat or enjoy each other's company without a word for long periods of time.

Finally the pirogue was finished and they spent many happy afternoons poling through the numerous bayous of the half-drowned land. Although they drifted along with little sound, blue herons and white egrets rose at their approach. Now and then a gator moved or opened enormous jaws, but they felt fairly safe in the pirogue.

When Jim was twelve years old his father took him, with John and Rezin, to Natchez to sell the cotton. It was a slow but exciting trip over boggy country, where often pine boughs had to be cut to make a solid enough bottom for the wagons loaded with cotton bales and driven by the slaves. The boys rode beside or ahead of the wagons, each carrying a pistol and a knife thrust in his belt, for often thieves or Indians waylaid the caravans.

Finally, without meeting a single robber or Indian, they came in sight of Natchez. Brown bluffs two hundred feet high rose on each bank of the Mississippi. On one side stood the white, columned mansions of Natchez-on-the-Hill, which took Jim's breath away with their grandeur.

He went to the levee and saw the mountains of baled cotton heaped on the slow-moving barges floating down the mighty river on the way to New Orleans. He saw his first cotton engine, which deafened him with its hurried chugging and clattering.

"Engine! Gin," he shouted above the noise. "I see now why they call it a cotton gin. Why don't we get one on our place?"

"Maybe we will one of these days." His father bent down to shout in Jim's ear.

The three boys roamed along the water front of Natchez-under-the-Hill where the houses were tumble-down shacks.

"Keep your hands on your knives, my pardners," Jim said. "I hear these water-front toughs will cut your throat for a silver dollar. I've already spent mine, so I don't need to worry."

"You'd better worry," John said. "The scum around here would kill you first and search your pockets afterward."

They spent half a day wandering up and down the shore, watching the barges being loaded. Half-naked Negroes heaved bales of cotton as though they were pillows. There was tobacco, too, and cattle and hogs—all bound for New Orleans.

"That's a place I must see someday," Jim said, speaking softly, as though to himself.

"I've got a feeling that you'll see a lot of places in your lifetime," Rezin told him.

"I hope so. Now we'd better go find Pa or he'll tan our britches for being gone so long."

They found their father at the Bristol House where they had taken lodgings for the night. He was talking to several men. Jim heard him say, "I can hardly believe it. You say that Fulton actually made a boat sail by means of steam—without sails?"

One of the men nodded. "Up the Hudson. I saw it with my own eyes. Fulton's Folly, men called it, while he was working on it. But Fulton had the last laugh."

"I'll be glad when we have steamboats on the Mississippi," Mr. Bowie said.

He turned and saw his sons. "I was beginning to wonder about you lads," he said. "How about supper?"

Jim was relieved to see that his father had not had time to worry about them. Evidently his day's business had been successful for he was in a jovial mood and ordered a whopping meal for the hungry boys.

Chapter Three

"OUR FORTUNES FOR TO SEEK!"

☆

It had been a long time since Jim had slept in a real bed. At first he rather missed the crisp crackle of the Spanish moss which filled his mattress at home, but he was so tired he soon fell asleep. It seemed that he had scarcely closed his eyes when his father was shaking his shoulder, ordering him to get up.

" 'Tisn't light yet, suh," the boy protested.

"We're starting anyway," his father said in a low tone. "I sold the crop for a good price and I've got two bags of money. A couple of mean-looking fellows were watching me last night as though they were planning some evil. I want to be well on our way before they're up."

Jim got into his linsey jeans, shirt and fringed buckskin jacket in no time.

"I've some food in my pouch," his father said. "We'll eat on the way."

Zeb had their horses saddled and ready by the time they stepped out into the cool air. They set out slowly so as not to awaken those still asleep on the hill, but away from the lodging house they urged their horses into a fast gallop.

"Where're the wagons?" Jim asked.

"I sent Tom and the other men out to sleep in them on the edge of town. They were to get up early and start. We'll overtake them."

Jim was relieved to hear this. If they were to be waylaid by highwaymen they might need a strong force. His heart was beating fast.

"Slow down," his father said.

Jim obeyed.

Mr. Bowie shifted his own saddlebags to the front of Jim's saddle. "These hold the money," he said quietly. "You're just a boy. Thieves won't expect you to have it. You have the fastest horse. If we're attacked, let Fleetfoot feel your heels. Keep going as fast as you can. Don't stop to fight. Understand?"

Jim nodded, not too happily. Already he had imagined himself the hero of a bandit attack, fighting like a demon with knife and pistol. It seemed not a bit heroic to be singled out as the one to run away when the battle started.

They finally overtook the empty wagons. At noon they rested their horses and ate lunch. While they waited Jim grew restless and drew out his knife for some practice throwing.

"Why, Jim!" his father exclaimed. "You're very good at handling a knife!"

"He practices all the time," Rez said. "When he isn't swinging the lariat he's throwing that knife of his."

"That's a good skill for a frontiersman." Mr. Bowie nodded approvingly. "A knife is quicker than a gun and often more useful. I'm glad to see you boys learn skills which might someday save your lives. You've got a good head on your shoulders, Jim. I've a notion you'll do all right."

Jim was so set up by his father's praise that when they set forth again he wanted a few bandits to appear so that he could send his knife straight through the heart of the leader. But the return trip was quite uneventful.

The pleasant days raced by. When no excitement offered itself, Jim and Rezin made it. Now they were closer to each other than ever, for John was a grown man and had gone into business for himself, buying and selling land. To add excitement to their hunting expeditions they roped deer, then one of the boys would leap from his horse and cut the throat of the captured animal. They also caught wild horses, just for the fun of it. Sometimes they let the animals go, or they would pull some promising steed home for the Negro boys to break.

One day, however, Rezin's knife slipped and gashed the palm of his hand to the bone.

"Drat it!" Rezin cried, wrapping his handkerchief around his hand to stop the flow of blood. "That's no way for a knife to behave. I've got to figure out a way to make one that won't slip. This will stop me from hunting for a while."

"I'm afraid it will!" Jim cried. "Let's get home quick so Mom can fix up your hand to keep you from getting blood poisoning."

While waiting for his hand to heal Rezin made drawings of a knife which would prevent a man's hand from slipping down upon the blade.

When he had finally drawn one to scale which suited him, he took it to Jesse Cliff, the plantation blacksmith. "Can you make me a knife like this, Jesse?" he asked.

"I'll do my best," the smithy promised.

A few days later Rezin proudly showed Jim his new weapon. It was an ordinary, single-edged hunting knife with a wooden handle, but with a straight bar between handle and blade.

"It's a dandy," Jim said admiringly, taking the knife in his hand. "Your hand won't slip onto the blade with this. That's sure. But is it balanced in throwing?"

"Try it and see."

Jim flipped the blade back over his shoulder and with a swift snap of the wrist sent the knife hurtling toward a knot in a log of the fence. The blade made a singing sound as it flew and a clink as it hit.

The brothers looked at each other in triumph. It took considerable strength to wrench the knife loose from its mark.

"Wow!" Jim cried. "What a knife!"

"Get the smithy to make you one," Rezin said, tucking his weapon into a sheath at his belt. All his life he would carry the scar on his palm which led to the making of the first crude Bowie knife.

Jim intended to go to the blacksmith, but cane-cutting time had come. Every hand on the place, including himself and Rezin, were busy from daylight until dark in the canebrake. Jim was wielding a knife, but not in a way he enjoyed.

He hacked away with rhythmic strokes. He had taken off his shirt and the strong muscles rippled under his bronzed skin. He was over six feet tall now and "strong as a young steer," his father proudly said. This work was not especially wearying, just monotonous. Jim's thoughts roamed. He was seventeen. A man. What would he do with his life?

His father was prospering on the plantation. Now there was a large new house with glass windows instead of oiled skins. Elvie Bowie had her own carriage to take her to Opelousas to shop or visit friends on near-by plantations. Life was pleasant here, but it was becoming too peaceful. He and Rez had to roam far afield to find excitement. Besides, it was time they were getting out on their own. Jim had no desire to carry on this business which his father had built up. Merely riding a fine horse over acres of plantation to oversee the work held no attraction for him.

He and Rezin had not discussed the future at any great length. Yet each knew pretty well what was in the other's mind.

The bell clanged from the big house summoning the Bowie men to the noon meal. When Jim and Rez reached the house they stood under the great live oak and pumped water from the well, drinking deep and throwing gourdfuls of the cool liquid on each other's heads. They pulled on their linsey shirts before going in to eat.

A strange carriage stood in front of the house, the horse tied to the hitching post.

"Mom's got company again," Rezin remarked.

"Evidently," Jim said. "It would be a dreary day if no callers came to the Bowie plantation. I don't feel up to company manners today. Besides, I smell sweaty as a horse. Let's get Mammy Lou to fill our plates and bring 'em out here and eat under the magnolia tree."

"Good idea." Rez grinned.

"Fill our plates heaping full," Jim directed Mammy Lou. "We're hungry and want to eat outdoors. Please tell Mom that we're too dirty to come to the table."

The cushiony Negress chuckled. "Mammy Lou'll give you plenty to eat and make excuses to yore ma. Seems to me, though, that since you have to stoop to come in the door, yore too grown up to keep tied to Mammy Lou's apron strings any more."

Jim patted her shoulder. "You know you love having us young'uns underfoot. You're going to miss it terribly when we cut loose. And it won't be too long."

Mammy Lou began to sniff. "It's the Lawd's trufe. So it is. Marsa John's already growed up and moved away. Miss Sarah married. Now you and Marsa Rez growed up —talkin' about leavin'. Ain't been no babies at this house for a long time. The rest will be leavin'. . . ." She picked up the corner of her apron to wipe her eyes.

"Now, now, Mammy Lou!" Jim said. "We're not gone yet, and Dave and Stevie'll be around for a long time. You'd better hurry and get the meal on the table. I heard Mom's bell tinkle a bit impatiently. Here, I'll fill our plates. You go and take care of the folks in the dining room."

When the two brothers had gorged themselves on Mammy Lou's fried chicken and biscuits, with yams, fresh peas and grape jelly topped by peach pie, they lay back with their hands under their heads.

They were under the open dining room window and the sound of voices reached them. They paid little attention until they heard their own names.

Their mother was speaking. "I wish you could have met my sons," she said. "Mr. Bowie and I are very proud of them. John, the eldest, is the steady one of the family— a successful business man. Rezin is the most brilliant. He can sit down and dash off an exceptional speech or bit of writing. Jim, two years younger, is a born leader. He's inclined to be bold and reckless though. Not afraid of anything in the world. However, I suppose time will steady him."

Jim and Rez looked at each other and grinned. "Eavesdroppers are supposed never to hear good of themselves." Jim chuckled.

"Unless," Rez drawled, "it's their mothers who happen to be doing the talking. It's a good thing mothers see the best in their children. The world at large won't be so kind in its judgment, I reckon."

"I suppose not," Jim answered. "When are we going out on our own, Rez? It's about time."

"I've been thinking the same thing. Funny how we always seem to have the same thoughts. How shall we set out to conquer the world?"

"There's a small sawmill for sale down on Bayou Beouf," Jim said slowly, "with a world of cypress and pine all around. The way this country's building up, there'll be a big demand for lumber. And merchants at New Orleans are clamoring for it. We can raft our logs through the bayous to the Mississippi. We ought to make good money. I'm sure that Pa'll back us and we can have him paid back in no time."

"Got it all thought out, haven't you?" Rez said, smiling. "When do we start being lumber barons?"

Chapter Four

A RUGGED LIFE

While on a business trip, John came to spend the week end with his family. During the long lazy Sunday afternoon the brothers talked. When he heard of Jim and Rezin's plan to operate a sawmill on Bayou Beouf, John said, "You weren't planning to leave me out, were you? I thought we were a threesome."

"We used to be," Jim said. "But you're doing all right on your own now. After all, you're older than we are. We'll both have to start from scratch, just as you did. We'd planned to ask Pa to stake us."

"No need of that," John insisted. "I've done right well on land deals. I've got money to invest. I'll go in with you and finance the deal. As you know, I'm pretty hardheaded so I expect to get my money back with interest in a short time. You boys, though, have enough energy and ambition to make it go."

Not only did John back his younger brothers financially, he also helped clear a patch of land and fell and saw timber for a comfortable but simple cabin. It was backbreaking labor in the languid southern air, with the sun beating down mercilessly.

This primitive life was well suited to the temperaments of "those wild Bowie boys." The arm of the bayou reached far into the backwoods in real wilderness area, yet it was an easy day's ride to Alexandria. The only humans the boys saw were the Acadian boatmen, called

Cajuns for short. These Frenchmen were *couer du bois* and usually their approach on the rafts or long pirogues was heralded by song ringing through the forests. Then John, Rezin and Jim stopped working and waved to the happy *voyageurs*. Sometimes they hired the Cajuns to raft their lumber to some market, but as yet they were not so overwhelmed with business that they were pushed to fill orders.

They cut thousands of feet of cypress, oak and ash and finally the boatmen made a regular habit of stopping to take on the lumber for Baton Rouge, New Orleans or other markets. They charged such a large commission, however, that the Bowies were dissatisfied and decided to find their own markets. One of them must go to New Orleans. John said he was too busy with his various land deals. Rezin was the logical one to go.

"You have a way with you," Jim said earnestly as he and Rezin paused to mop their sweaty brows. "You're the best talker and have the most polished manners."

"As if any son of Elvie Bowie would grow up without polished manners!" Rezin remarked. "You have a magnetic personality, Jim, whether you realize it or not. You're the one to go."

Jim's heart missed a beat. It had long been his dream to visit that exciting city, yet he did not want to appear too eager for fear Rezin cherished a similar wish.

"Ho!" he scoffed. "You're afraid you'll miss a Sunday with the lovely Miss Margaret Neville."

Rezin grinned. "You've guessed it," he admitted. "I'd really like to take in the sights of New Orleans with you, but we can't afford to have both of us go anyway. And right now I seem to be making some headway with Miss Maggie, although the beaux buzz around her like bees around a honey tree. But who can blame them? Isn't she the prettiest young lady you ever saw?"

"She's pretty all right." Jim tried to sound enthusiastic. "I don't blame you a bit if you've fallen in love. I wish you luck. . . ." His voice trailed off. His heart wasn't in what he was saying. Since Rez had taken up courting he was detached and Jim felt left out and lonely.

Although hewing down trees and sawing them into lumber with a whipsaw was the hardest sort of physical labor, the Bowie boys still had enough energy for wrestling, gator riding and wild steer roping. Whenever they needed game for food they would not consider getting it by so dull a method as shooting it. No. They must mount horses and chase the game, then rope it, after which Rezin would gallop up, slide from his horse and neatly cut the animal's throat with his new knife.

Thus danger lent spice to the food they ate. The Cajun boatmen who chanced upon the "wild Bowie boys" riding roped gators stared goggle eyed at such crazy sport.

Now and then Elvie Bowie rode in her carriage to the small clearing on the bayou, bringing Mammy Lou with baskets of civilized food. Then the old Negress cleaned up the cabin to make it "fitten for young gentlemen."

John was gone for longer and longer periods of time, for his business was growing. Rez and Jim were still unusually comradely and evidently it was only Jim who noticed the widening breach in their relationship. He knew that when Rezin married things could never be the same again. Naturally his main interest would be in his bride and later in his own family. Jim tried to suppress his jealousy, but he had long moments of silence when he was morose and almost bitter. At such times he wandered off alone into the woods or got into the pirogue and poled his way through shadowy caverns of foliage.

One day, smoothly and silently, he was making his way up a stream he had never before traveled. Although he tried to make no sound with his pole to disturb the birds or the deer which came to the water's edge, his passing awoke a napping alligator. It gave an angry flip of its tail before it sank to the bottom of the stream.

The splash caused a beautiful egret to fly into the air. Immediately a man leaped up at the water's edge and shook angry fists at Jim. "*Mon Dieu! Sacrébleu!* Awkward oaf! Why for do you disturb the holy silence of the forest? You spoil my loveliest picture."

Jim rested his pole against the bottom of the water to stop the pirogue while he stared in amazement at this small and angry man.

"Don't sit there looking so stupid. Why do you not explain?" the stranger demanded.

Jim suppressed a chuckle and said politely, "Please pardon me. I did not realize that you owned this wilderness."

The man's anger seemed to evaporate. "You will pardon me, please," he said contritely. "Of course I do not own this wilderness. It belongs to God. And to the birds—the beautiful, wonderful birds. I was painting the one that just flew away. I was almost finished."

"I'm terribly sorry, suh," Jim said. "I didn't know there was another human being within miles. I certainly didn't expect to find a painter here."

"Come and see what you have spoiled."

Jim clambered out of the pirogue. The little man led him to an easel under a spreading oak tree.

Jim whistled in sincere admiration. "Am I seeing a painting or an actual bird?" he asked. "If that one on canvas should take off and fly away, I wouldn't be the least bit surprised."

The painter grinned. "You like, then?"

Jim nodded. "It's amazingly lifelike!"

"Look. I show you the others." The stranger picked up a portfolio and proudly leafed through pictures of various birds, all done with exquisite detail.

"You are a fine artist," Jim said sincerely. "What is your name, suh?"

"John James Audubon. And yours?"

"James Bowie. But surely you don't live about here or I would have heard of you. You must be famous."

Audubon sighed and closed his portfolio. "Alas no! The public has little interest in birds. They want anyone who can wield a brush to paint their vain, simpering women in satins and laces. That I have to do in order to eat. My Lucy and I teach the young ladies and gentlemen how to dance." He held up an imaginary skirt and pointed his toes daintily and bowed and pranced until Jim roared with laughter.

"And all I want is to paint birds. I leave my lovely Lucy and my young Victor at home whenever we have a few pennies ahead. She teaches the dancing while I wander the forest—painting, painting, painting. It is for this I live. It drives me." He clasped his head dramatically as though the something which drove him caused intense pain.

"You are a genius, suh," Bowie said. "My brothers and I would be proud if you would accept the hospitality of our cabin while you are in this region. You didn't tell me where you are from."

"New Orleans. The Queen City."

"Fine!" Jim exclaimed. "You can tell me about it. I

plan to make a trip there soon to try to find a market for our lumber."

The artist stayed several days as the guest of the Bowies, using their pirogue to go into the waterways in search of birds. His flimsy clothes were neat but patched in several places. He was extremely thin and from the way he devoured the food it was evident that he had not had enough to eat for some time. It did the generous-hearted Bowies good to stuff him with fish, fowl and wild game.

Jim and the artist set out early one morning on horseback. They planned to ride across country until they reached the Mississippi where they would take a boat. While they jogged along Audubon told Jim about New Orleans.

"It is a strange and wonderful city," he said. "Like no other American city, for it is a mixture of French and Spanish. Americans are regarded as foreigners. First founded by the French in 1718, it became the capital of the immense colonial empire of Louisiana.

"Most of the population had come from France," he continued, "and they retained the French language and customs. The city was isolated from the rest of the country and the citizens scarcely knew or cared when the American Revolution was fought.

"Then in 1769 the people of New Orleans received a terrible shock. They learned that six years earlier France had sold Louisiana to Spain. The first intimation the New Orleanians had of this transaction was when twenty-four Spanish men-of-war appeared in the harbor, carrying the officials who had come to occupy and govern the city.

"The Spanish rule was not strict and for the most part the people went on living much the same as before."

Audubon said, as they jogged along the shady trail. "French language and customs still prevailed, although some Spanish was spoken.

"It was during the Spanish rule that smuggling was introduced," he went on. "The Spanish rulers tried to put severe rules about trading into effect, but the French loved to fool their masters and so smuggling became a game in which everyone indulged. Privateers who raided Spanish ships were looked upon as heroes and merchants vied to buy their merchandise.

"You know, of course, that Napoleon, desperate for money, sold all of Louisiana to the United States in 1803. Although now an American city, the citizens of French or Spanish blood, called Creoles, look down upon all Americans as crude savages. Quarrels are frequent between the two factions. And, according to the code of the day, dueling is the accepted and only honorable way to settle such quarrels."

"What about this pirate Lafitte?" Jim asked. "I've heard about him. He must be a daring fellow."

"My dear friend!" Audubon said in mock horror. "Never call the great Lafitte a pirate. He's a privateer, he'll have you know. He has letters of marque from the Columbians allowing him to raid enemy Spanish ships wherever he finds them. And he does. With amazing daring. He is the most famous privateer of the day. It's a well-known fact that the blacksmith shop his brother Pierre runs is a hangout for smugglers who trade in his merchandise. His main hangout, though, is down on Barataria, below the swamplands. There, they say, he lives like a king."

"That," vowed Jim Bowie, "is a place I must see."

Chapter Five

MEETING WITH THE PIRATE JEAN LAFITTE

Audubon insisted that Jim Bowie be his guest at his New Orleans home. He met the artist's sweet, cheery wife Lucy, and his lively, dark-eyed son Victor. They lived in a modest, one-story log house, the walls of which were decorated with Audubon's wonderful bird pictures at which Jim would stare by the hour.

"My husband is a very great genius," Lucy said proudly. "The world does not yet appreciate him. In time it will—but alas, perhaps not until after he is buried! His pictures, though, will live forever. For that I work myself to such skinniness teaching the rich Creole belles to dance so that we will not starve while my James paints."

"Your husband seems to be in great demand as a portrait painter," Bowie remarked.

She shrugged. "At that he might become rich—but it is not so important. There are many who can paint portraits, but only one Audubon, the bird painter."

Bowie found that his friendship with the artist opened doors to him in New Orleans that would otherwise have remained closed. To the haughty Creoles he was a "foreigner," ignorant and uncultured like all Americans.

But he went about with Audubon on his portrait commissions to plantations and homes and so met the upper classes, although scarcely as a social equal. Jim discovered that his clothes were all wrong. When he saw the finely clad Creole dandies looking down their noses at him he went to the finest tailor in New Orleans and ordered skin-fitting trousers of soft tan wool, a long-tailed waistcoat and satin vest imprinted with roses. He added to this outfit a high collar, wide flowing cravat and white beaver hat, and felt he was ready to meet the young Creole gentlemen on their own grounds.

He went with Audubon to a great plantation where the artist was to do the portrait of the seventeen-year-old daughter Eliza Pirrie.

Miss Eliza acknowledged the introduction with a graceful curtsy and a beguiling display of dimples. Her blue eyes frankly admired Jim's wide shoulders and great height. She looked disappointed when he said he was an American.

"I had hoped you were French," she said, giving him an arch look.

"Is it such a disgrace to be an American?" he asked a trifle stiffly. "I'm very proud that I am."

"But of course," she said. "I have no doubt there are many well-born Americans, too."

He shrugged. "We consider a countryman well born if he's a good citizen."

She broke into delighted, tinkling laughter. "You big American!" she cried. "You are so different. You make the dainty Creole gentlemen I know seem silly."

This was a new experience for Bowie. He had not met many young ladies and none who gave him such an excited, important feeling.

"Shall we go on with the sitting?" Audubon threw a chill over the little flirtation.

Bowie watched for a while, but at last he grew restless and strolled about, admiring the beautiful curved stairway which joined two galleries, the rich carpeting, the high ceilings, the brocaded satin draperies, the gleaming silver and the glittering crystal chandeliers. Beautiful gardens and smooth lawns surrounded the house. An air of serenity, peacefulness and gracious living hung about the plantation.

It was the same in the city. Jim had already wandered through the fascinating *Vieux Carré,* or French quarter, where the houses were built flush with the banguette, or sidewalk. Negro women shuffled along balancing huge bundles on their heads. Housemaids saved themselves steps by doing their shopping for groceries by means of a bucket and rope. Numerous peddlers of pralines and other sweets wandered through the streets with their wares on boards hung around their necks. He admired the lace ironwork which adorned most of the fine homes. Now and then he caught a glimpse through a partly opened gateway of sunny courtyards beautiful with flowers and foliage. He was eager to see inside the tantalizing paradises.

At length Jim got the opportunity to visit two of the finest homes when Audubon went to paint portraits. In both places the elders greeted him coldly, making him feel like an intruder. The young Creole dandies looked him over critically, although Jim had a notion that they envied his broad shoulders and great height. Most of them were short with absurdly small hands and feet. The young ladies of the families, however, stared at him with frank admiration. Everywhere he went he was impressed by the easygoing air, unhurried and relaxed. Here indeed was gracious living.

"I'm enjoying myself immensely," Bowie said one day as they returned home after a day of portrait painting.

"But I must get about my business, and find a market for my lumber."

The artist spread his hands in a hopeless gesture. "Alas, my friend! There I cannot help you. I know no purchasers of lumber. I gain entry to the homes of the rich Creoles merely to paint the empty faces of their empty women. Bah! What a waste of time! My birds are waiting in the forests, wondering why I neglect them. But my Lucy and Victor must eat. And somehow I must earn money to publish my book of bird paintings."

"I wish I were rich," Bowie said. "I'd publish it for you."

"Ah, my generous friend! And I cannot even find anyone to buy your lumber."

"Don't worry, suh," Bowie told him. "I'll stir myself and find a buyer. You've been showing me such a good time that I've been neglecting the business I came for."

Early next day Jim went to the water front to try to find someone to buy his lumber. On his way he passed through the *Vieux Carré* and upon numerous lamp posts he saw this sign in big letters:

PROCLAMATION

I DO SOLEMNLY CAUTION ALL AND SINGULAR AGAINST GIVING ANY KIND OF SUCCOR AGAINST *Jean Lafitte* & HIS ASSOCIATES: BUT TO THE AIDING & ABETTING IN ARRESTING HIM & THEM, AND ALL OTHER IN LIKE MANNER OFFENDING, & DO FURTHERMORE, IN THE NAME OF THE STATE, OFFER A REWARD OF $500 WHICH WILL BE PAID OUT OF THE TREASURY TO ANY PERSON DELIVERING *Jean Lafitte* TO THE SHERIFF OF THE PARISH OF NEW ORLEANS, OR TO ANY OTHER SHERIFF

IN THE STATE, SO THAT *Jean Lafitte* MAY BE BROUGHT TO JUSTICE.

GOVERNOR W. C. C. CLAIBORNE

Jim saw a man with a wide grin on his face standing under one of the signs. His arms were folded across his chest and his whole attitude was one of open defiance. A group of men stood watching him and whispering among themselves.

"Well, here I am," the man said. "Why doesn't someone go tell Claiborne that I, Jean Lafitte, dare him to arrest me?"

No one moved. So this was the famous Jean Lafitte! Jim saw a slim man with broad shoulders. His dark eyes were restless and the lid of one of them drooped, as though in a half wink. His hair was dark and glossy. His high-cheekboned face was handsome and he looked more a gentleman than a pirate. There was a forceful, arrogant manner about him, and Jim instantly sensed a spirit dynamic and untamed.

Bowie stepped up boldly and held out his hand. "I've wanted to meet you, suh," he said. "I've a feeling that we might be kindred spirits."

Lafitte's keen eyes swept over him. Finally he thrust out a hand and Jim's hand was squeezed in a warm grip. "I like your looks, young man. You have force. What is your business?"

"I'm in the lumber business, suh. I came to New Orleans to see if I could find a buyer. But I don't know anyone here."

"Look up Martin Bel on the water front," Lafitte told him. "Say that Jean Lafitte sent you. He's contracting to build many of the fine mansions in the American section, and is in the market for hardwood. I'm sure he'll buy from you."

"Thanks, suh. I'm very grateful."

The piercing gray eyes narrowed. "You say you cut this wood yourself—you and your brothers?"

Bowie nodded.

"It must be hard work."

"It is."

"You are too intelligent to work like a slave. Do you want to make a great deal of money quickly?"

"Yes. Of course, suh."

"Then come to see me at my place at Barataria. We can do business. I should like you to be my guest."

"Thank you, suh. I'll plan to do that."

"Do so. Very soon."

He moved away from his post beneath the sign toward the Lafitte blacksmith shop. Bowie hurried to the water front to look up Martin Bel, who agreed to buy all the cypress and oak the Bowie brothers could deliver within the next year.

The following day Jim went back to the *Vieux Carré* on his way to the Lafitte blacksmith shop hoping to find the privateer in order to thank him for the favor. He noticed that the signs offering five hundred dollars for Lafitte's arrest had been torn down and in their places were other notices offering fifteen hundred dollars for the arrest and delivery of Governor Claiborne to Jean Lafitte.

Everyone was laughing over the placards and Jim himself was amused. He vowed that he would certainly accept Lafitte's invitation. The man interested him. Besides, he was burning with curiosity to know what sort of business deal Lafitte had in mind. Probably something along the order of smuggling which, though illegal according to the governor's edict, had become an accepted sport indulged in by the most respectable citizens of New Orleans.

Chapter Six

VISIT TO THE PRIVATEER STRONGHOLD

John and Rezin were pleased with the success of their brother's trip to New Orleans. With a market for all the hardwood that could be cut, they were ready to plunge into the labor of procuring it. But Jim was restless and dissatisfied and hated the work more every day.

One day he loosened his hold on his end of the whip-saw and mopped his forehead. "There must be some easier way than this!" he burst out.

"Easier than what?" Rez asked.

Jim waved a hand at the boards they had sawed and the hated tool with which they had done the work. "To make money. We work harder than any slaves we know. In New Orleans I saw a new way of life. People living in beautiful homes, wearing fine clothes and having time to enjoy life. That's what I want. And I don't want to wait until I'm an old man. Rez, we've got to figure out some way to make a lot of money in a hurry."

Rez shrugged and drawled. "I'm with you, Jim. Start figuring. Got anything in mind?"

"Nothing definite yet." Jim's tone was impatient. "But I've made up my mind. Nothing'll stop me."

"John's been doing well buying and selling land," Rezin pointed out.

Jim nodded. "That may be the answer. To the west of us are millions of acres which can be bought cheap.

I'm sure there's going to be a strong, steady expansion to the west since President Jefferson bought all of Louisiana from Napoleon. He sent Lewis and Clark out to make a report on the new territory, you know. I've also got a hankering to see Texas. I'll use my wits to buy up likely sections and sell them at a profit as civilization moves westward."

His eyes held a faraway expression. "But first," he went on, "I want to pay a visit to Jean Lafitte's hideout. When he invited me he hinted that he might have some money-making deal for me."

With a chuckle he sank to a log to rest and motioned his brother to sit beside him as he told how the New Orleaneans delighted in outwitting those in authority by dealing in smuggled goods. The Lafittes were the leaders in this sort of business.

Jim said, "I wouldn't care to engage in smuggling myself. But I can see how a man of Lafitte's caliber would find delight in outsmarting a man like Claiborne. I've an overpowering curiosity to see Lafitte's hideout."

"Then let's go," Rez said.

"First," Jim responded, "let's get rid of this place. We'll ship our lumber off to Martin Bel, according to my agreement. Then we'll put our sawmill and the acres we've cleared up for sale. That should give us a nice nest egg of working capital to go on."

Jim knew of the mysterious Barataria country south of New Orleans, where Lafitte's headquarters had been located. In his pirogue he had explored portions of this watery area, the haunt of wild things. From Louis Gasperon, a Baratarian who sometimes worked at the Bowie sawmill, Jim learned more of the region and of the activities of Jean Lafitte.

Louis himself greatly amused Jim and Rezin. He wore a bright red head scarf and large brass earrings. Although actually a mild-mannered man he tried hard to look like a pirate. He was proud of the fact that he often worked for Jean Lafitte, as many of the Baratarians did. For many years Spanish, French and Portuguese people had lived quietly along the waterways of the Barataria in small fishing villages. They were for the most part gentle, religious folk, although the swamplands formed ideal hiding places for those who wanted to escape the law. When the Lafittes adopted Grand Isle and Grande-Terre as their headquarters, the Baratarians took up smuggling, too, along with trapping and fishing.

Jim well knew the circumstances which made this a ripe time for privateering to thrive. Mexico, Central America and South America were all in revolt against Spain. The republic of Cartagena, a seaport of Colombia, accommodatingly issued letters of marque against Spanish shipping. The Baratarians, armed with cannons and cutlasses and with these letters to give legality to their actions, then sailed from the numerous byways of the swamplands to capture and loot Spanish ships. And right at their back yard was New Orleans with a wealthy population of about thirty thousand. It was also the gateway to commerce of the whole Mississippi Valley.

Early in 1813 the New Orleans merchants became so disturbed over the inroads the smugglers were making in their business that they appealed to the naval authorities for help. Louisiana's Governor Claiborne meantime posted the proclamation which branded Jean and Pierre Lafitte as "banditti and pirates."

Yet within a few months desperate New Orleaneans would be begging those same "banditti" and pirates to help them. Jim chuckled when he heard the story. In 1812 the United States declared war upon Great Britain. The Louisianians, however, felt remote from the battle until 1814 when two English officials boldly went to Jean Lafitte's headquarters at Grande-Terre and offered him thirty thousand dollars cash, a captaincy in the British navy and an opportunity for each of his men to enlist if he would organize the Baratarians to help capture New Orleans.

Jean Lafitte asked for time to consider the proposition. Then he straightway sent a message to the American officials informing them that the British were planning to besiege New Orleans and telling of their offer to him. He furthermore offered to organize the Baratarians in defense of the city.

When Andrew Jackson reached New Orleans and saw the desperate situation, he immediately called upon Jean Lafitte and the Baratarians, who joined forces with the Americans and swung victory to their side.

"To think," Jim told Rezin, "that I had to miss all that excitement! I'm more determined than ever to accept Lafitte's invitation to visit him."

"If this deal to sell our place goes through, I'll certainly go with you," Rezin said eagerly.

The place was sold and the Bowie brothers made a profit which amazed them.

"Maybe we've found the secret for quick wealth," Jim chuckled as he counted the money. "Buy a piece of uncleared land for a song, improve it a bit, then sell it for several times what we paid for it."

They engaged Louis Gasperon to guide them, since they wanted to travel by pirogue through the Barataria to the Gulf. Louis was sure that he could get them passage on some ship going to Galvez-town, Lafitte's present headquarters.

They followed one waterway after another, through many bayous and marshes, a strangely wild and beautiful region.

"The trembling prairie," Louis called it. It was difficult to tell where dry land left off and water began. Mostly it was swampland with a jungle growth of high grass and shrubbery. A blue mist hung over the place, giving it a strange, eerie look.

"What a wonderful place to get lost!" Jim shuddered slightly as he saw a water moccasin slither into the water from the tall grass.

He and Rezin were both alert, trying to memorize landmarks in case they wanted to make their way here again without a guide.

"The Temple." Louis' waving hand indicated one island much larger than any others they had seen. Great oaks circled a central clear space. "Lafitte held his auctions there for smuggled goods and slaves. Many merchants and planters from New Orleans came to bid for his goods."

Jim laughed. "The New Orleaneans love to break the laws the American officials make. Ever since it was made illegal, traffic in slaves boomed more than ever. Blackbirding became an accepted way of making a living, just as smuggling did."

"A silly law if there ever was one," Rezin said hotly. "How can men run plantations—raise cotton and sugar and tobacco without slaves? And the black men are better off on fine plantations where they receive good care and are taught and trained as Christian, civilized beings."

Jim nodded. "Often when we were working the whipsaw I envied Father's slaves. It makes me tired to hear these narrow-minded Yankees carry on about the evils of slavery. Most of the slaves we know are very well treated."

"Louis," Jim asked, "why is Jean Lafitte so bitter against the Spaniards? I believe him when he says that he is a privateer, not a pirate; that he has a letter of marque from Cartagena making it legal for him to prey upon Spanish ships. But he does it with such relish. Why does he hate them so much?"

"That is a story to wring your heart," Louis said. "Once he was rich enough to buy and outfit his own ship with merchandise. About the same time he fell in love with and married a beautiful French girl. They set out to sea for the American coast but were captured by a Spanish man-of-war which took over his ship and set Lafitte adrift in a small boat. He was later picked up half dead from starvation and thirst by Baratarian fishermen who nursed him back to health. Later he learned the sad fate of his lovely wife. Believing that Lafitte had a fortune hidden somewhere, they put the young woman to the torture and she died as a result. So-o, who can blame our captain for carrying on unceasing war against the Spanish?"

"That explains it," said Jim. "No wonder Lafitte hates the Spanish."

Now it was easy enough to distinguish water from land. They had reached Barataria Bay which was sprinkled with little islands. The largest, Grande-Terre, had been Lafitte's headquarters and a large house, now deserted, still stood there.

Louis learned from his fisherman friends that a boat would embark for Galvez-town, or "Campeachy" (Campeche), as Lafitte called the island port of the Mexican state of Coahuila.

Coming in sight of Campeche around the curve of the Gulf of Mexico, Rezin and Jim stared eagerly at the amazing tall red house surrounded by as motley a collection of dwellings as could be imagined. Some were made of palmetto, others of canvas and a few of stone or wood. Ships and small boats were anchored in the harbor.

"The Maison Rouge," Louis said, pointing to the bright red building, the second story bristling with cannon. It was on a high dune at the back of the town and obviously served as a fortress as well as a dwelling.

"Since he moved from Barataria, the scum of the earth have taken up with our Captain Lafitte, men who would murder you for gold."

"Fortunately we haven't any gold," Jim said calmly. But he thought of the six thousand dollars he and Rezin carried in their money belts, and involuntarily put his hand on his knife.

Louis did not miss the gesture. "You'll be safe enough with Jean Lafitte," he said. "The men respect and fear him."

As they approached the large house an immensely fat man, with a long black pigtail hanging between his shoulders, waddled down the walk. At his ears dangled enormous earrings. About his monstrous middle was a sash of bright red and in it was thrust a huge, ivory-handled knife. A sword in a sheath hung beside it.

"Dominique You," Louis Gasperon said, "this is Jim Bowie and his brother. Jean Lafitte met Mr. Bowie in New Orleans and asked him to be his guest."

Dominique You gave them a genial smile and tried to

bow but was prevented by his too-fat stomach. "Follow me," he said, walking ahead and up the steps onto the wide veranda and into the house. "Wait here. I'll call the captain," he said, and he waddled from the room.

The Bowie brothers stared around in amazement. Here was a room with heavy timbers of weathered mahogany. On the walls were beautiful tapestries and at the windows hung the finest of brocaded draperies. The floor was covered with rich rugs. Silver and crystal glistened on tables and shelves.

"Are we in some sultan's palace?" Jim whispered.

Then quickly both were on their feet for Jean Lafitte had entered, his footsteps silent on the thick rugs.

"Ah, Mister James Bowie!" he called cordially. "How nice of you to accept my invitation and to bring your handsome brother. I am most happy to have you as my guests."

He turned to the three men who had followed him. "You have met Dominique You," he said. His clipped speech held only the slightest trace of French accent. "This is Beluche and here is Nez Coupe, who was most unfortunate to lose his nose in a saber duel. His opponent, needless to say, met a much worse fate."

While the Bowies were acknowledging the introductions to the lieutenants, Lafitte pulled a bell rope and almost instantly a servant entered bearing a tray of sparkling cool wine which the Bowies found most refreshing.

"René," Lafitte said, "show my guests to the front bedroom. After you wash up, gentlemen, join me here and we will dine."

Jim and Rezin found their room as fine as the rest of the house

"The houses I saw in New Orleans were furnished no better than this," Jim said, speaking in a whisper for fear someone might be spying.

"No doubt the loot from many a ship has gone into these furnishings," Rezin likewise spoke softly. "It's all very luxurious, but I don't exactly feel at home here."

Their luggage had been brought up and the two guests changed into their best garments, for Lafitte was garbed in fawn-colored breeches and waistcoat and brocaded vest.

Lafitte led them into a long dining room where a mahogany table gleamed beneath the light of numerous candles in silver holders. They dined on roast wild turkey and on a delicious mixture something like a dish Jim had tasted in New Orleans called "bouillabaisse," and on candied fruits. Never had Jim tasted such a meal.

"You live in great comfort here," he remarked.

"Why not?" said Lafitte. "The comforts of life were made for those who have the perceptions to enjoy them. You . . ."—his sharp eyes bored into Jim's—"are, I discern, such a person. And your brother, too. Tonight we will chat. You will rest. Tomorrow we will tour the island. See the sights—such as they are."

Again Jim was conscious of that boring look, as though Lafitte were trying to pry into his soul. It made him slightly uncomfortable.

Chapter Seven

BLACK GOLD

☆

In the morning after a sumptuous breakfast Lafitte said to his guests, "Gentlemen, do you care to join me in a walk about my premises?"

"We will be pleased to," Jim replied.

Nez Coupe and Dominique You followed. They seemed always to be with their captain.

A weird sound as of mournful singing came from the upper end of the island. Rounding a bend Jim saw an enclosure built of high logs.

"The barracoon," Lafitte said. "I presumed you gentlemen would like to see it."

"The slave pen?" Jim was conscious that again the captain was giving him that strange, questioning look. "Do you have slaves there now?"

"A ship brought some yesterday," Lafitte replied, his tone casual.

"Do you have trouble disposing of them now that the law has made their traffic illegal?" Rezin asked.

Lafitte laughed. "The Louisianians like nothing better than breaking Yankee-made laws. No. It's very simple to sell slaves. And immensely profitable. I sell them at a dollar a pound. Whoever buys them takes them to the settlements and informs the official that he found someone dealing in slaves. Then they are auctioned off and the informer is given half of whatever they bring. Usually he or his agents bid them in. Then whoever bought them from me originally sells them to the planters."

Again Jim met Lafitte's crafty stare. He was beginning to understand what sort of business deal the privateer had in mind for him.

When they reached the barracoon, an overseer turned the key in a great padlock and the gate swung open. Jim could scarcely suppress a gasp at what he saw—the most miserable human beings he could possibly imagine. They sat against the fence, chained to its logs, although Jim could not see why they should be, for certainly they had neither the strength nor the energy to try to escape. They had stopped their mournful singing at the sight of the man who owned them, and sat staring at the ground.

"These are in bad shape," Lafitte admitted. "As I said, they just came in yesterday. I haven't had time to fatten them. Poor creatures. They evidently suffered in the hands of their captors—the Spanish dogs."

The pen was indescribably filthy and a sickening stench rose in the hot enclosure.

"I've seen enough," Jim said curtly, turning away.

"They often arrive in this condition," Lafitte said. "Don't be shocked. In a few weeks they will be fat and sleek on some rich man's sugar plantation. You have seen how they fare."

"If the poor creatures live that long." Jim bit the words off shortly.

"They'll live, if they get out in the open soon enough," Lafitte said. "That's the trouble. They aren't used to being penned up. If they have to be kept that way long after an ocean trip during which they are half starved, it's just too bad."

"How much do you want for them?" Jim stopped in his

tracks and stared at Lafitte. Rezin had caught up with them.

"A dollar a pound," Lafitte replied. "To simplify matters and make it round numbers, I estimate an average of one hundred and forty pounds per slave."

"I'll buy the lot," Jim snapped. "At your price. If you will also sell me supplies for the poor devils to live on until we can get them into the hands of humane owners."

"Mr. Bowie! Do you mean to imply that I'm not humane?" Lafitte's eyelid came down in that queer wink, and Jim did not know whether he had actually taken offense or was laughing at him.

"You're in this business for what you can get out of it," Jim replied shortly. "I realize that you aren't responsible for the condition of those creatures. And you haven't room here to turn them out."

Lafitte shrugged. "I consider I'm doing the poor devils a favor by taking them from the Spanish dogs and turning them over to men who will treat them humanely." Again the wink.

"Jim!" Rezin broke in. "Do you realize if you do this you will be a blackbirder?"

"Aren't you with me, Rez?"

"Well, I'm not sure that I like the idea too well."

Jim turned to Lafitte. "Do you mind if my brother and I discuss this matter alone for a moment?"

"Of course not. You gentlemen join me at Maison Rouge when you have reached your decision."

"I don't like the idea of being a blackbirder, either," Jim said. "But it would haunt me forever to go away from here and leave those black people in that filthy hole. I'm going through with it. I'd like to have you with me, but if you aren't I'll go it alone."

"You know I'm with you," Rezin said.

The business transaction was completed after the Bowie brothers went to their room and took the needed cash from their money belts. Lafitte had his men outfit some small boats at the mouth of the Calcasieu. Jim, Rezin and Louis Gasperon transported their "black gold" by water to Calcasieu Lake, then marched them overland.

It was early morning when this land trek began. Each Negro was clad in cheap linsey breeches and carried on his head a week's supply of food, wrapped in sacking. Louis walked at the head of the procession, leading the way. Rezin and Jim brought up the rear, each with a rifle cradled in his arm. The slaves gave them no trouble. They seemed relieved to be on the move and in the open where the air was clean and fresh.

Arriving at the border of the United States, Jim found that it was as ridiculously easy as Lafitte had promised. He reported that he had discovered a camp of slaves in a near-by forest and led the officials to the spot. Of course the captors were nowhere to be found. The slaves except for the six they kept for themselves were sold at auction and Jim and Rezin Bowie were given half the amount, eighteen thousand dollars.

They bought a new plantation in Rapides Parish, near Alexandria. With the slaves to clear the land they built a house, for Rezin was engaged to Margaret Neville and eager to be married.

Soon Jim received word from Lafitte that another load of slaves awaited him. He asked Rezin to go with him to get them.

"I've got all I want, Jim," his brother said. "Maggie's against this sort of thing, and I wouldn't risk losing her for all the money in the world. We've a fine plantation here. Or it will be in time."

"That way takes too long!" Jim cried. "I haven't your patience. Besides, I haven't any Maggie to lose. I'm going it alone, Rez."

"Good luck to you!" Rezin said.

Jim turned away. So their paths were finally separating. Rez wanted to settle down to being a family man and to the humdrum work of running a plantation. Well, such a tame life wasn't for Jim.

Louis went with him to Galvez-town and again Jim bought forty blacks. Now, even more than on the first trip, he realized that every foot of the way was fraught with danger. He and Louis each had a rifle and a knife, but two men would have little chance against forty Negroes if they decided to turn on them. He chained them at night; otherwise the slaves were free to plod single file through the tall grass and marshy ground. They were completely docile, however, and gave him no trouble.

Three times he traveled to Campeche and brought back slaves. And strangely enough, each time he was gone tragedy struck the Bowie home. The first time his brother David was seized with cramps while in swimming and drowned. Next, his sister Sarah died in childbirth. The third time he returned home to find the family mourning the death of his father.

Mrs. Bowie had gone to live with Rezin, Maggie and their two small daughters at Arcadia. She called Jim before her.

"What is this I hear about you, Jim?" she asked, staring up at his six-foot-two.

"I don't know. What do you hear?"

"That you have turned blackbirder. Is it true?"

He felt like a small boy about to be chastised for some wrongdoing.

"It's true," he said. "Don't tell me, Mom, that you have turned against slavery."

"It's an economic necessity for the South," she said. "But what you're doing is illegal. I raised my sons to be gentlemen. I will not have you doing something which will brand you as less than one."

"Are you ashamed of me, Mom?"

"Yes, I am. So ashamed that I can't hold up my head among my friends." She put her hand before her face and wept. That was the undoing of Jim Bowie. He had been about to tease her about her inconsistency. But he had made her ashamed and the knowledge turned like a knife in his heart.

He put his arms around her. "Don't cry, Mom! Please. I'll never do it again. I wouldn't humiliate you for the world."

"Oh, Jim!" she sobbed. "I do so want to be proud of my sons. And you—the one I expected the most of. I was always sure that you'd make me proud of you."

"And I'll do it, too, Mom," he promised. "You'll never be ashamed of me again."

Chapter Eight

A LEGEND GROWS

Jim Bowie was on his way to becoming a legend. Already he looked like the sort of person of whom one would expect heroic deeds. Handsome and dynamic, he towered head and shoulders above the average man. Wherever he went, eyes turned his way. His work at the whipsaw had made his shoulders massive. His hands were huge and incredibly strong. His reddish hair, always slightly tousled, gave him the look of a man in a hurry to do important things. His eyes, sometimes gray, sometimes blue, according to his mood, had a compelling look.

He had made over sixty-five thousand dollars running slaves and at twenty-five was considered rich. With his brothers he owned three prosperous plantations and had numerous other land holdings. They had set up the first engine for making sugar from cane.

Having given up trading in slaves to please his mother, he returned to Alexandria, now a booming town crowded with land speculators. Cotton and sugar were bringing swift wealth and the westward expansion Jim had prophesied had begun.

He and Rezin sold one of the plantations and immediately bought other land with the proceeds, then borrowed more money for more land.

Jim was welcome at the finest homes. Now there were many mansions similar to those on the plantations around

New Orleans. He was continually on the go, traveling on horseback or by stagecoach, buying or selling lands or playing the gallant gentleman at social functions.

With characteristic wholeheartedness he threw himself into the political dissensions which were then bubbling with white-hot fury in Rapides Parish. Two factions had sprung up and were fighting each other with deadly rivalry: the Old-Timers, who had conquered the wilderness and therefore considered it their right to rule it; and the New-Comers, whom the former considered upstarts but who seemed determined to take the reins of government into their own hands. The southerners' regard for background and tradition and the New-Comers' lack of such regard was to bring about an inevitable clash.

Norris Wright, a frail-looking young man, came from Baltimore to work as clerk in the general merchandise store. In spite of his appearance, he was a man to fear. Already he had fought five duels and killed two of his adversaries, seriously wounding the others. He was shrewd, calculating and ruthless.

The Old-Timer sheriff of Rapides Parish died in office. Before citizens realized what was happening young Norris Wright was appointed to fill the vacancy. When Wright was up for election Bowie campaigned zealously against him, agreeing with his friends that it would not do to allow the upstarts to gain the political saddle. Wright, however, was elected. In no time at all he became the political leader of the New-Comers. He helped organize a new bank and was elected to its board of directors.

"Seems to me," Jim remarked ironically to Rezin, when he heard this, "that for a young man, comparatively new to the community, he's coming up mighty fast. And there are indications that there was skulduggery about the election."

Rezin nodded. "I wonder how that will affect our standing at the bank."

"It shouldn't matter much." Jim shrugged.

He stooped down to kiss his mother. "Take care of yourself, Mom," he said. "I'm riding to the sugar plantation. Some trouble has developed with the new steam engine. Then I have business in Natchez."

He mounted his fine blooded horse and galloped through the rows of trees, delighting to see the improvements on all sides. It gave him great satisfaction to realize that he had had a very active part in developing this lovely country.

Passing one of the newer plantations he slowed down so that he could see what had been done there. The mansion was nearing completion. Jim nodded approvingly. The tall pillars rising from ground to balustrade were in the traditional southern style, the proportions of the great white house were correct and pleasing. He wondered what sort of person the owner was.

He was not long in finding out. Rounding a clump of bushes he came upon a sight which sent him into one of his swift rages. A Negro was tied to a tree and a brawny white man was beating him unmercifully, although the unfortunate slave seemed near unconsciousness—or death—with blood streaming down his back.

Jim leaped from his horse and, snatching the whip from the man's hands, started laying it onto the erstwhile flogger. "Anyone who would treat a defenseless slave like that should be shot!" he cried.

The man, who was nearly as tall as Bowie, managed

to seize the lash and the two stood panting and glaring at each other, pulling at opposite ends of the whip.

"What business is it of yours what I do to my own slave?" the man demanded.

"I make it my business when I see a human being mistreated," Jim replied.

"This slave's no good," the man blustered. "He deserved a flogging."

"No creature on earth could deserve such a beating as that." Jim let go of the whip. "You would have killed him before long. I'll buy him from you. How much do you want for him?"

"He's not for sale."

"You say he's no good. If that's the case, you should be glad to get rid of him."

A shrewd gleam came into the man's eyes. "Twelve hundred dollars will buy him," he said.

Jim whistled. "A pretty price for a slave that's no good."

He drew out his wallet and wrote a check for the amount. The man accepted it. "So you're Jim Bowie," he said. "I've heard about you. My friend Norris Wright has often mentioned you."

"Indeed?" Jim said, stepping over to untie the bonds of his newly acquired slave. He made no further comment, realizing that probably whatever Norris Wright said about him was not complimentary.

He led the Negro over to his horse. The black man could scarcely walk. Bowie half lifted him behind the saddle before he mounted.

"My horse is strong enough to carry double the short way back to the plantation," he said.

"God bless you, massa!" the Negro murmured. "I'll make you a good slave, as God is my witness."

"What's your name, boy?"

"Sam, suh. Big Sam, they calls me."

"All right, Big Sam. Do your best for me and we'll get along."

He rode back to the home plantation and left Big Sam in Rezin's care, to have his wounds treated. He did not know it then, but he had acquired more than a slave; he had gained a man who would worship his rescuer all his life.

Jim continued his trip toward Natchez, stopping to visit various friends on their plantations. One of these was Dr. William Lattimore, an owner of a large estate and a highly respected citizen.

"By the way," Jim said as he was preparing to leave, "where's young Bill? I missed him."

Dr. Lattimore chuckled with indulgent pride. "Bill's getting to be quite a man. My political duties take me away so much I'm training him to take over. I sent him to Natchez the other day to sell the cotton. Time he took some responsibility."

"Good idea," Jim said, mounting his horse. "Bill's a fine lad. He won't disappoint you. Good-by until next time I see you."

"Look Bill up when you get to Natchez," Dr. Lattimore said. "He'll be disappointed to have missed you. He is stopping at Roseleigh Manor."

"I'll make it a point to do that," Bowie promised.

It was late at night when he reached Natchez. Arriving at the inn he inquired about young Lattimore, but was told that he had not yet come in. On his return from supper, Jim saw a tall figure walking ahead of him with an unsteady gait.

Catching up with the man, he saw that it was Bill Lattimore. "Why, Bill Lattimore! What luck! I've been looking for you."

"Oh, Jim Bowie! It's good to meet a friend after being in a den of thieves." The young man moaned and would have fallen if Jim had not caught him.

"What's the matter, Bill? Are you sick—or drunk?"

"Both—I guess. Oh, Jim! I've done a terrible thing."

"Suppose we sit here on the inn steps and you tell me about it," Jim suggested.

The young man sank down and put his head in his hands. "I can never go home. I've disgraced my father."

"Come now!" Jim said, "things can't be that bad! Tell me what happened."

"I lost my father's crop money. Every cent of it. He trusted me. Depended upon me . . ."

"You've been to Natchez-Under-the-Hill." Jim hazarded a guess.

The young man nodded.

"I can take up your story from there," Jim went on. "You stopped somewhere to buy a drink. You met a friendly, likable chap who bought you another drink, then suggested that the two of you see the sights. Feeling in an adventurous mood you agreed. Your new acquaintance then led you to one of the dives under the hill. You were offered more drinks. Then you were neatly fleeced by experienced crooks. I've heard that story many times."

"What a fool I was—the farmer boy out to see the sights. I'll never face my father after this, Jim."

"That's nonsense." Jim rose. "Come with me, Bill. Take me to this place where you got fleeced."

"Oh, no, Jim! I won't have you doing that."

"Won't have me doing what? You don't even know what I have in mind—if anything."

"I—I was afraid you planned to go there and try to make them give my money back. You might get hurt. They're a rough lot."

"Why don't you just leave things to me, Bill? After all, I'm rather experienced. I've been around Natchez a bit and know it 'on' and 'under' the hill. I'd really like to see this particular place and I promise you that Jim Bowie can take care of himself."

"Well, if you insist." Bill got to his feet reluctantly.

"I do insist. However, I'll bet I know which dive it was. Did you happen to hear the name Sturdivant mentioned?"

"Yes!" Bill cried. "That's it. They called it Sturdivant's place."

Jim groaned inwardly. John Sturdivant was the most notorious of the desperadoes who made Natchez-Under-the-Hill their haunt, and his henchmen were the toughest there were. Yet it was considered the thing to do by fashionable gentlemen on the hill to frequent these gambling dens from time to time. Jim had followed the fad with his young friends, so knew the various houses, although he did not care for such amusement.

He knew that Sturdivant was a dangerous man. Called "Bloody Sturdivant," he was one of those who used the then-prevalent dueling code as a pretext for getting rid of his enemies. He was deadly with both pistol and knife and had several killings to his credit. Besides, it was known he had burned to the ground the homes of four of his political enemies.

Jim Bowie strode into Sturdivant's gambling house

with white-faced Bill Lattimore at his heels. At one of the tables Jim pushed Bill into a chair and pulled out a roll of money. "Play this as if it were your own," he whispered into his young friend's ear.

Jim stood watching with a nonchalant air while the game went on. Bill won, then lost, won slightly, then began to lose steadily. Jim's eyes were half closed as though he were about to fall asleep, but he was not missing a movement of the dealer's fluid hands.

Finally he yawned, stretched and nudged Bill. "Give me your place for a while or I'll fall asleep."

The game went on silently for a time, Jim winning then losing. Suddenly he reached across and seized the dealer's hand. "Put that card back!" he said in a threatening tone. "I saw you palm that ace."

He rose, pushed back his chair and calmly pulled the money on the table toward him and put it in his pockets.

"Hey there!" John Sturdivant bellowed. "You can't do that in my house."

"Yes I can," Jim said calmly. "I caught your man cheating. A little while ago one of your confederates brought this man here and robbed him of all of his father's crop money. I don't stand for that sort of thing being done to my friends—here, or anywhere else."

"Put that money back!" Sturdivant roared.

"I took only enough to repay my friend for what you stole."

"You can't call me a thief."

Jim stared the gambler straight in the eye. "I did call you one, suh," he said in a gentle voice, but there was nothing gentle in his eyes.

"You won't leave here with that money without fighting for it," Sturdivant's voice quivered with anger.

"Then we'll fight. What weapon do you choose?"

Sturdivant jerked out a knife. Bowie took his from its sheath.

"We'll fight with our wrists strapped together," Sturdivant declared.

"Very well." Jim shrugged.

While the chairs and tables were pushed back the two contenders had their left wrists bound with a buckskin cord. All color was drained from Bill Lattimore's face as he watched.

Complete silence fell over the room while the antagonists faced each other. Then one of the croupiers started counting slowly, "One, two. . . ." When he said "three," knives clashed and there was the sound of shuffling feet as the men thrust and parried. Bowie made a sudden lunge and Sturdivant's knife clattered to the floor. Jim's thrust had cut the tendons of his wrist.

Sturdivant's face turned white. He tensed, bracing himself for the death blow. Instead Jim slashed through the buckskin bond. "I'm not killing you," he said. "I wouldn't kill a defenseless man. I reckon, though, that I've cured you of knifing men for a while at least, Sturdivant."

Pushing Bill Lattimore before him, he left the room in a deliberate manner, but as the door was closing behind him he heard Sturdivant's vicious tone, "Get that man, Bowie! Do you hear me! You three get him—or you'll be accountable to me."

Jim opened the door and peered inside. "I promise," he said in a level tone, "that I won't be so generous to whatever poor devils you're sending after me, Sturdivant. I've never yet provoked a fight and never will. But I'm ready for those who come after me."

He and Bill were allowed to ascend the hill safely.

Young Lattimore lost no time in spreading the tale of Jim Bowie's first duel. And the tale lost nothing in the retellings. From it sprang absurd variations, for James Bowie was the sort of personage about whom legends gathered.

Chapter Nine

THE BLOODIEST DUEL

After his fight with Bloody Sturdivant people called Jim Bowie the Young Lion. He laughed at the name, but it so fitted his courageous and fiery personality that it stuck.

For several years Jim and Rezin had been making money from everything they touched. Then a streak of ill fortune hit them. For three years in a row crops were bad. The following year their lands were flooded.

"What shall we do, Jim?" Rezin asked, as he stared at the inundated land.

"Our credit has always been good," Jim said reassuringly. "We'll go to Alexandria and borrow money to tide us over until we get good crops again."

"I hope you're right." Rezin's worried frown eased a bit. "You go and attend to it, Jim. I'll stay on the plantation and see about things here."

Next day Jim rode to Alexandria and asked for the loan. He thought he noticed the bank president, long a friend, hesitate as though embarrassed. "I'll have to take it up with the board of directors, you know, Jim," he said.

Bowie nodded. "I'll drop in tomorrow and get the money."

He was not prepared for the shock he received when he stepped cheerily into the bank next morning.

"I'm sorry, Jim," the banker said. "But the directors turned down your application."

"Turned it down!" Jim's tone was incredulous.

"I was in favor of it, of course," the banker went on. "But I couldn't swing enough of the other directors."

"Who opposed me?"

"I'd rather not say."

Jim's brows met in a deep frown. "You don't need to tell me. I know. It was Norris Wright, wasn't it?"

The banker nodded.

"I would expect him to be against me. But since when and how has he got so much power that he overrules the rest of you? Some of you are my friends."

"I don't understand it myself," the banker said unhappily. "That man does wield power. And it is growing."

"It's going too far." Jim rose and gripped the back of the chair until the knuckles of his great hands showed white. "The man's a rascal. I'm satisfied he bought the election which made him sheriff. And a man who steals votes will steal money. Not only that. His friends are allowed to commit murder safe in the knowledge that they won't be arrested."

The banker nodded. "You refer to the scandalous Crain affair, of course. I agree with you, Jim, that things are going too far. The feud that's been simmering so long between the Old-Timers and the New-Comers is bound to come to a head someday. And I'm afraid that someone will be killed."

The Crain affair to which Jim had referred had added considerable fuel to the smoldering feud between the two factions. Colonel Robert Crain from Virginia had rented a plantation on Bayou Rapides. He straightway took sides with Norris Wright and proceeded to cut quite a swath in and about Alexandria, both socially and politically. Despite his exaggerated southern gallantry, he ignored his debts. When any creditor attempted to collect an overdue account he flew into a rage and instantly challenged him to a duel.

When his landlord went to collect the rent, the colonel offered to give him a note.

"I prefer cash," the landlord said.

Thereupon Colonel Crain pulled out his pistol and shot the man for "insulting a gentleman from Virginia."

The Virginia "gentleman" was accused of stealing a neighbor's slaves and taking them from the state. It looked as if the colonel was about to be indicted, but Norris Wright pulled political strings and quashed the proceedings against his friend. There were many similar incidents.

Jim Bowie happened to be in Alexandria on business during this tense time. Dressed in a suit of fine broadcloth and wearing a high beaver hat he was unarmed. Rounding a corner he came face to face with Norris Wright.

He bowed slightly and would have hurried by, but Norris seized his arm. "I've heard the things you've been saying about me." His usually pale face was flushed with anger. "You wouldn't dare say them to my face."

"You're wrong," Jim replied calmly. "I'm willing to say anything to your face that I'd say behind your back. I said that you stole the election which put you in the sheriff's office. I said that anyone who would steal votes would steal money."

Wright whipped out his pistol and fired. Jim saw the blaze and knew that for a moment he was slightly off balance but he felt no pain. Suddenly all of the enmity for this unprincipled man that he had been holding in leash bubbled to the surface. With a bellow he threw himself at Wright and seized his throat between his strong fingers.

Friends jerked at his arms, but his grip held.

He heard Rezin shout, "Stop, Jim! You're killing him."

After he had been pulled away, he saw two men supporting Norris Wright. Jim's anger drained from him and he turned away—shocked at what he had almost done.

His own knees nearly buckled and his friend Dr. Denny came to help Rezin bolster him up. Jim put his hand to his side, then drew it away covered with blood. "Looks like he hurt me more than I thought."

"Come to my office," the doctor said.

They found a flattened silver dollar in Jim's vest pocket, which had deflected the bullet. It had only grazed Jim's ribs, making a painful but not serious wound.

"Of course you'll call Wright out for this," the doctor said.

Jim shook his head.

"Don't you believe in the code of honor?" the doctor asked.

"Not to the extent of provoking fights," Jim said. "I nearly killed Wright with my bare hands. So far as I'm concerned, that evens up things between us."

"If he challenges you, though, Jim, you'll have to fight," Rezin said.

"I suppose so, or be branded a coward for the rest of my life. But I've got a feeling he won't be too anxious to meet me again."

Jim was right. No challenge came from Norris Wright, yet the Alexandria street fight between them fanned the white-hot embers of the feud.

Rezin gave Jim his knife—the one with the guard

between handle and blade. "Wear this always when you go away from the house," he said seriously. "After what happened, you would be a fool to go about unarmed. A knife is more dependable than a gun. Sometimes a gun doesn't go off, but a knife will never fail you if you're quick enough."

Then into the tense atmosphere was dropped an explosive morsel of scandal regarding General Montford Wells, a prominent citizen. He traced the origin of the gossip back to Dr. Maddox, also prominent in the Wright faction. Naturally the gossipmonger was challenged to a duel.

Elaborate preparations were made for this "medley," as duels were often called.

The Vidalia sand bar, a long, heavily wooded peninsula reaching into the Mississippi, was chosen as the dueling ground. In the center was a barren circle whose sands had already been drenched with the blood of those who believed in the "code of honor" to settle personal differences.

Dr. Maddox chose as his seconds Major Norris Wright, Colonel Crain, who settled his debts with bullets, Crain's son-in-law Alfred Blanchard and Alfred's brother Cary. Dr. Denny would go along as his surgeon.

Sam Wells selected his brother Tom; Jim Bowie chose General Cuny and George McWhorter, a prominent planter. His surgeon was Dr. Dick Cuny.

Never were the potentials for serious trouble so neatly gathered. Tom Wells had been shot by Alfred Blanchard. Jim Bowie had been shot by Norris Wright and in self-defense had nearly strangled him. General Sam Cuny had shot Colonel Crain in the arm when the latter was trying to collect a defaulted note.

At dawn on September 18, 1827, the two groups of grim-faced men walked quietly up the dark street and boarded the ferry to Vidalia. Walking in pairs they reached the sand bar just as the sun was rising. The trees were tipped with rosy gold. Birds sang. Otherwise there was no sound but their footsteps crunching through sand.

The seconds of each side withdrew to opposite positions behind clumps of bushes. Jim found a place where he could peer between branches and see what was going on.

Dr. Maddox and Sam Wells, the two principals, stood facing each other at ten paces. At the count of three both pistols blazed. Neither man was hit. Once more both weapons spat fire. Again no one was hit. Sam Wells stepped forward, hand outstretched. Honor had been satisfied.

Jim bit back an impulse to laugh. He had been keyed up for so long that the idea of a bloodless duel after so much tension struck him as deliciously funny.

He emerged from behind the bushes and stepped up beside General Cuny. "A fortunate ending for a duel." He grinned.

Cuny put a hand on Jim's arm. "I'm not so sure it's over," he gasped. "Look!"

Jim stared in the direction toward which Cuny pointed and saw Colonel Crain striding toward them, a black look of hatred on his face. His hand lowered toward his pistol. He drew and fired at Cuny, but missed. Jim felt a blazing pain in his hip. He had no gun, but drew the big knife Rezin had told him to wear and advanced toward Crain, who had drawn another pistol. The colonel fired again, this time killing General Cuny.

Seeing his friend fall, Jim's grip tightened on his

knife handle. Dragging his injured leg, he continued his advance. Crain brought his pistol down on Jim's head.

The world broke apart in blinding pain. Blood from a gash in his scalp poured into his eyes. He wiped it away with his coat sleeve and struggled to his feet, the knife held menacingly before him. The sight was too much for the "gentleman from Virginia." He turned and ran into the bushes.

Still dizzy and unsteady from the blow on the head, Jim mopped the blood again from his eyes just in time to see Norris Wright coming at him with a sword cane upheld. Bitter hatred was graven on those foxlike features.

Wright lunged. Jim tried to parry the blow with his knife blade. He missed then, felt the sharp blade rip through his chest. He fell on his back, but struggled to rise. Wright put one foot on Jim's chest in an effort to pull out his sword. The blade broke. Jim reached up and gripped Wright's arm, as he tugged at the sword. Just as the handle broke off, Jim's knife came up, slashing Wright's abdomen, and the Wright-Bowie feud was over. Jim tried to rise, but a bullet from another direction hit him in the arm. He fell again and consciousness was blotted out.

Jim Bowie felt as though part of him were floating in space, yet pain gripped every inch of his body.

"He'll be dead before morning," he heard a voice say.

Were they talking about him?

"Four serious wounds," the voice went on. "He lost more blood than any man can stand to lose and live. That sword just missed his heart." Jim Bowie heard the words, but he was too tired to open his eyes. Nothing seemed to matter.

"What a medley!" the voice went on. "Norris Wright and Sam Cuny dead. Jim here as good as dead. Crain and Blanchard wounded. That's the bloodiest duel ever. One that'll go down in history."

"It should be a duel to end all duels." It was Rezin's voice with a bitter note in it. Jim recognized it. Yet he could not summon sufficient strength to move or speak.

"Jim won't die, Dick," Rezin's voice said. "You aren't reckoning on that marvelous stamina of his."

Good old Rez! Jim thought as he slowly sank again into unconsciousness. Of course he wouldn't die! He would fool that prophet of doom whose voice seemed so far away.

Chapter Ten

A MAN AND HIS KNIFE

James Bowie did not die, but there were weeks of delirium while his pain-wracked, blood-drained body lay in a friend's home in Natchez and his life hung in the balance. Later Dr. Cuny told him it was a miracle that he was alive.

Rezin was there, as he had been nearly every day since the historic duel on the Vidalia sand bar.

Jim chuckled. "I was half dead when I heard you and Rez discussing me. You said I couldn't live. Rez said I would. And I made up my own mind right then that it would be a good joke to fool you, Doctor."

"I was never happier to be mistaken," his friend replied.

"Never forget," Rezin's tone was deadly serious, "that it was a knife that saved your life. The knife that I gave you. Never be without it."

"I won't." Jim's seriousness matched his brother's. "I've been doing a lot of thinking while I lay here. And much of that thinking was about your knife. I worked out a design for improving the knife. I hope I never have to kill another man. But I intend to be ready to defend my own life if need be."

Soon he was strong enough to return with Rezin in the carriage to Arcadia. It was spring and the air was heavy with the fragrance of the waxy magnolia blossoms. He strolled about the lovely gardens with Rezin's pretty little daughters. Later he was able to ride a horse. Always Big Sam rode at his side. Each day the rides were longer until he could sit for an hour or so in the saddle without breaking out into a cold sweat from weakness.

Now that he had begun to mend, his tremendous vitality reasserted itself.

Every day he whittled models of the knife he had designed in his mind while convalescing in Natchez. Finally he had one that suited him. He showed it to Rezin.

His brother turned it in his hand, critically studying every detail.

Finally he nodded approvingly. "It's good," he said. "I'll take it to Jesse Cliff in the morning and have him make it in metal."

Jim shook his head. "This isn't a job for our plantation smithy. This knife must be made by an expert craftsman, with a genius for working metals. It will be something special." His long fingers caressed the wooden model.

"Where will you find such a metalworker?" Rez asked.

Jim stared off into space, a dreamy look in his gray eyes. "There is such a man," he said. "I heard about him in Natchez. He served an apprenticeship as a silversmith, went west and settled at Washington in Arkansas where he set up a blacksmith shop. His partner takes care of the rough work of the Southwest Trail, while he tends to mending guns and making knives. His name's James Black."

"That's quite a distance to go to get a knife made."

"I'll stop on my way," Jim said. "I'm planning to take to the Chihuahua Trail soon. I want to look into the land deals that are opening up there in Arkansas. Texas still appeals to me. I want to take a look-see out there. I've sat around here being lazy long enough."

Rezin looked at him and sighed. "I figured that the wanderlust had you again. Wish I could go with you. But I can't go traipsing off and leave Maggie and the girls. But of course John and I are with you financially. We Bowie boys will stick together always. And if anything extra exciting comes up, I might manage to be with you for a time."

Jim grinned. "I'll make it a point to find some venture to hold you to that promise."

"I suppose you have in mind buying up some Spanish land grants," Rez said.

Jim nodded. "Why not? It's more or less of a gamble, I suppose. But not too much of one. The population is pushing westward. If we buy up land cheap and then sell at a profit, how can we lose?"

"I'll always hold Arcadia as our stronghold," Rezin promised. "I've got a feeling that you'll make money for all of us. But in case you don't, there'll be Arcadia to come back to. Consider it your home as long as you live."

A mist blurred Jim's eyes. "That's mighty good of you. But somehow the wide open spaces pull me mighty strong. I aim to take Sam along, and we'll take our time and look the places over. It's plenty wide. It should give a man room to grow."

Within a week Jim was on his way, galloping along on a fine chestnut horse with Big Sam followed him on another and leading a pack animal.

Jim felt the powerful animal under him and the wind brushing his face. This was Living—to be traveling once again the Adventure Trail! Strength and zest raced through his veins. He was glad to be putting behind him the artificial plantation existence. It held no challenge. The slaves did all of the work while the gentlemen and ladies, dressed in fine clothes, gave balls and hunts and gossiped in the Natchez or Alexandria coffee shops. It was all very well for a time. Jim grinned when he remembered how he had once envied that sort of life and had bent every effort toward achieving it. But when that goal was won it seemed tame and flavorless.

Would it always be that way? he wondered. Would he always be dashing off toward some new goal only to find it dull and tasteless once his aim was achieved? At any rate, there was a thrill in pitting his abilities toward new attainments.

They rode at a good clip over a well-defined trail which divided Arkansas into two sections. The southeastern part was level and neatly plotted off into cotton plantations. To the north lay thickly timbered hills where gaunt men and women lived in miserable cabins clinging to the hillsides. The condition of the trail showed the heavy travel of people pushing westward. He hoped he wouldn't be too late to get in on some good land deals.

Washington, he found, was quite a civilized town with substantial buildings and an air of prosperity. There was a better-than-average inn with good food and clean, comfortable beds.

After supper Jim lounged about the narrow lobby and asked the innkeeper if he knew of an ironworker named Black.

"Sure do," the man replied. "Has a shop right at the end of the street. He's busier than a cat on a tin roof in a hail storm. Can't keep up with the business coming over the trail. Keeps five slaves turning out knives, axes, plowshares, and the like. Mighty clever man. Works all day and sometimes into the night."

The following morning Jim strolled to the end of the street where he saw a big sign:

JAMES BLACK
IRONWORKER

Jim strode inside and stared around curiously at the three large forges where slaves, naked from the waist up, were blowing up the blazes with bellows or hammering metal on one of the several anvils. The place bustled with activity, yet there was neatness and order in the conglomeration of wagon wheels, tools, horseshoes and various articles to be mended.

He told one of the slaves that he would like to see Mr. Black.

"Yessuh. I go tell him," the Negro answering, disappearing behind a black curtain. In a moment he came out followed by a slim man who moved with quick steps.

"I'm James Bowie from Alexandria way. Even in Natchez your fame as an expert in tempering steel is known. I understand that you have a special method. . . ."

Jim stopped, realizing that he must have said the wrong thing, for it was as though the man had drawn a mask over his face.

"I do my best always," Black said. "But my methods are my own. In fact, not even my partner knows my secret. I work behind this curtain."

"Pardon me, suh. I have no wish to pry into your secrets. But I have a special job for you to do. I want you to make a particular knife. I've come many long miles to ask you to do this."

He drew the wooden model from his pocket. After examining it, Black said, "Come with me." He held aside the curtain so that Jim could enter into the space where he had a desk. Adorning the wall was a collection of finely wrought knives which made Jim's eyes sparkle.

Then his glance was drawn to the ironworker whose thin face was bent over the model. Jim noticed his long-fingered hands—the hands of an artist.

"Yes—yes!" Black said eagerly. "It is good. I will do it. I enjoy making fine knives. This I shall strive to make a masterpiece."

Jim drew out the knife Rezin had given him. "This weapon saved my life," he said. "But it's just an ordinary hunting knife with a guard. It's not good for defense. It's clumsy. As you can see, I want an extra thick heel to give the blade strength so it will not snap. The point must come at the precise center of the width of the blade, for balance. Notice that the blade curves to the point from both front and back. Both of these curves must be as sharp as the edge of the blade itself—which must be sharper than any knife you have ever made before."

"You leave it to me," Black said impatiently. "You will be satisfied, Mr. Bowie. Come back in two weeks."

"I must have it sooner than that, suh." Jim thought of the thick money belt he wore. He needed the improved knife as protection from border ruffians and highwaymen.

Black shook his head. "You ask for perfection, Mr. Bowie. I cannot do such a job in less time."

"I shall be back in two weeks." Jim bowed and let the curtain drop behind him.

Jim put in the time buying land grants. In two weeks he was back at James Black's shop, admiring the gleaming knife which the master cutler proudly placed in his hand. He tested the balance. But when he was about to check the keenness of the blade with moistened finger Black warned, "You'll cut yourself. Here, test it like this." He pulled out one of his own brown hairs, held it up and with a quick stroke neatly cut the slender hair in two.

"Well, I never!" Jim exclaimed.

He reached for the knife again, turning it in his hands, admiring the workmanship. The blade was fourteen inches long, single edged to the curve of the point, where both sides had been sharpened to a razorlike edge. The curve started two inches from the point. On the back of the blade was a parrying guard of hardened brass.

Jim's fingers stroked this guard which had been Rezin's invention.

"Hardened brass is a much softer metal than tempered steel," the ironworker explained. "So I made the guard of brass so it would catch and hold a blow. Otherwise your opponent's blade might slide and cut you."

Jim nodded and studied the two-pronged cross guard which was about three inches long. He noted that even the handle was a work of art, being of buckhorn dressed smooth where his hand would clasp it. On one side was a small silver plate with his name crudely engraved upon it.

"Mr. Black," Jim said. "This weapon is a masterpiece. I shall feel safe with it. I think that you've made a knife that will go down in history."

Black laughed, obviously well pleased with his work, but neither man had any idea how true those words would prove to be.

Jim found several land deals to his liking while in Arkansas and invested all the money he had with him, making it necessary for him to return to Alexandria to raise more funds. One evening he and Sam continued riding after nightfall in order to reach Rezin's plantation so that they would not have to sleep on the trail. Suddenly Jim's horse shied violently.

"Whoa, boy!" Jim spoke soothingly. He leaned forward and slid a hand along his mount's neck. He felt a coarse coat sleeve and realized that someone was holding the bridle. A shot rang out and sharp pain stabbed his leg.

Rough hands pulled him from the saddle and pushed him to the ground. Jim jerked his knife from the sheath and slashed upward. There was a cry of agony, then a great sigh and the hands eased from his shoulders.

Again someone seized him in the darkness. Again the knife slashed. Then there was silence except for the snorting of the frightened horses. Jim felt around for the reins and climbed into the saddle.

"Where are you, Sam?" He kept his voice low.

"Right here, massa." Jim could hear the thankful relief in his slave's voice. "Oh, praise the Lawd, you's all right, suh!"

"Follow me. Hurry!" Jim set his horse to a gallop.

Not until the following afternoon when he went to Natchez did Jim know that he was thought to be dead—killed on the trail by unknown highwaymen.

"That's strange!" Jim said after several friends had been amazed to see him limping around the streets. The shot he had received in the fleshy part of the leg was painful but not serious. "I can't understand why it should be known in Natchez that I was waylaid—unless whoever attacked me came from here."

Later in the afternoon word was brought that the

bodies of two men, recognized as Bloody Sturdivant's hoodlums, had been found beside the trail.

"It's plain now," Jim told Dr. Cuny, who was dressing his leg. "Sturdivant hasn't forgotten his threat to get even with me. But he boasted too soon that I was dead."

Later he went looking for Sturdivant, but the gambler was nowhere to be found.

Friends clamored to see the "Bowie knife" as it immediately was called. From that day on, cutlers were besieged with orders for copies. As for James Black, his reputation was made. He could not keep up with orders for this new weapon of the frontier—the knife which would carve for itself a niche in history.

Chapter Eleven

TEXAS ADVENTURE

Following his complete recovery from the terrible wounds suffered in the sand bar duel, Bowie felt a greater rush of ambition and energy than he had ever known. Nothing seemed impossible. He and faithful Big Sam rode back and forth between Alexandria and Arkansas, buying and selling land, or promoting land deals in Louisiana.

It was an exciting, adventurous era—one well suited to his temperament. As he had foreseen, already by 1829 the American tide had spilled over into Texas. The Mexican government at that time welcomed the energetic American settlers, stipulating only that they become Catholics and Mexican citizens. Stephen Austin's efforts at colonization were a success and prospects for ambitious settlers were bright.

Bowie perceived the shrewdness of the Mexican government's action in encouraging American settlement in Texas. The Mexicans themselves had been unable to cope with the Indian problem. Over those wide acres roamed the fiercest and cruelest Indians of the whole hemisphere: the Comanche, Waco, Caddo and the cannibalistic Karankahau. The very names of such tribes struck terror to men's hearts. Yet when did danger ever hold back Americans from seeking new goals? To Bowie it only served to lend spice to his ventures in Texas.

The early Spaniards, as he knew, had been brave

enough, yet they had failed to establish permanent settlements. Except for those at Nacogdoches and San Antonio de Bexar, their missions and presidios had been wiped out. No wonder the wily Mexicans decided to let the savages throw themselves against the Americans, who might subdue them to such an extent that the Mexicans would dare move in.

Jim found the Mississippi at Natchez crowded with great steamers, loaded to the gunwales with cargoes and settlers. There were immigrants fresh from Europe, and Americans whose fathers had pioneered the frontier and who were again pushing westward to new, uncrowded lands. Naturally Jim Bowie wanted to be with these adventurers on the trail blazed not so long ago by Davy Crockett and other Kentuckians like Daniel Boone, moving from "cramped quarters" looking for new "b'ar kentry."

There were gentlemen from the South in that crowd—many of education and culture. There were gamblers and river pirates, too, and others seeking to escape the consequences of a lawless past.

It was 1830 when Jim Bowie reached Texas—still a Mexican state, but where already the seeds of revolt had been sown. He had left Sam behind at Arcadia. Old age and "rheumatiz" had put misery in Sam's big bones and he could no longer keep up with his master.

Jim Bowie took his time looking over the land—the woods and streams and hills—the vast open spaces alive with buffalo and wild horses. Here was room enough for all he decided—Mexicans, Americans and Indians. His heart quickened with the realization that this was a region where many men would make fortunes. And he was in at the beginning! Certainly he would become rich—and a leader.

He rode to San Antonio de Bexar, the largest town in Texas. Established by the Catholic fathers in the days of the Spanish Conquest, the Spanish influence still predominated. It was the capital of the province, and Bowie found himself in a new world of leisurely living and charming customs. Strangers spoke to him smilingly as though he were a friend.

The city had two main squares, the Plaza de la Constitution which the *palacio* of the vice-governor faced, and the Plaza Militar where the soldiers' barracks were located. Jim was amused by the lack of military bearing of the Mexican soldiers. Their chief function seemed to be standing guard before the *palacio* of Juan Martin de Veramendi.

He wandered about the streets enjoying the sights. It was spring. The sun was warm and the flower gardens in bloom. There was an other-world charm about Bexar. The tree-lined San Antonio River wound through the city where Mexican women bent over the water, washing clothes. He was delighted by the pastel-colored houses built of thick adobe walls, the huge carved doors and barred windows of the *palacios*. Many of the finer homes were built around courtyards, as were the homes along the *Vieux Carré* in New Orleans. Now and then the great carved gates swung ajar showing gardens with gracious shade trees and tropical flowers.

He soon grew used to the groan of ungreased, solid wooden wheels drawing the overloaded *carettas*, and the clang of the church bells summoning worshipers to services nearly every hour of the day.

He roamed through the markets with their spreading

awnings beneath which peddlers lounged beside their wares.

He succumbed to the *mañana* atmosphere and found it restful for a time to let matters drift from day to day. *Mañana* would be soon enough to decide what he would eventually do. This much he knew: he liked Texas and intended to stay.

It surprised him that now and then men or boys he met on the street called him by name and some of the bolder youngsters asked to see his knife. He wondered how these people had learned who he was or about the Bowie knife. He did not realize that he was a famous person, or that the knife was already a symbol of heroism and daring and that schools for training men in the use of the Bowie knife had sprung up in New Orleans.

One day a soldier brought a note to his room. The paper was heavy with important-looking seals.

Written in Spanish, it was an invitation to visit Vice-governor Veramendi at his *palacio* the following morning.

"Tell the vice-governor that I shall be there," Jim said in Spanish.

After the messenger left, Jim asked himself what it meant? Obviously it was a command, but was it merely a social courtesy—or something more?

In the morning he got out his gray broadcloth suit, linen shirt, brocaded waistcoat and fine beaver hat. Although the *palacio* was only a short walk from his *fonda*, he rode horseback, for the Spanish were horsemen before all else. They had little respect for a man afoot.

The Veramendi *palacio* was a two-story stone building built around three sides of a patio which gave upon the river. Bowie was ushered into a large room with massive dark furniture and great oak beams across the ceiling. A man with glossy black hair, handsome features and piercing dark eyes rose as Bowie entered.

The vice-governor bowed in a courtly manner. "I am honored by your visit," he said.

"I was honored to receive your invitation." Jim's courtliness was a match for Veramendi's.

"Be seated. We will talk." The vice-governor motioned to a huge carved chair.

"You have been a visitor in Bexar for two weeks now." It was not a question but a statement of fact.

Bowie raised his eyebrows and merely nodded.

"You were a friend—or shall I say a business associate—of Jean Lafitte. You were victor in a famous duel. You invented the knife named for you and which has become the chosen weapon of nearly every man in the country."

A smile tugged at Jim's lips. "You know much about me, suh. I'm honored at your interest."

"What are your intentions in Texas, Mr. Bowie?"

The curtness of the question after such preliminary courtesy startled Jim. At first he resented such directness. After all, his business was his own. Veramendi didn't own Texas, he reflected, but it occurred to him also that the vice-governor was very powerful and could by a mere nod of the head cause him a great deal of trouble in a strange land.

"I haven't exactly made up my mind, suh." Jim decided to be perfectly frank. "Texas is a wonderful place with a great future. I want to become part of it. I want to help develop her riches and resources. On my way here I noticed vast cotton fields. In Louisiana my brothers and I set up on one of our plantations the first steam engine for making sugar. I wondered why something like that couldn't be used here—to make cloth without shipping it away."

Veramendi slapped his hand on the polished desk top and his face broke into a delighted smile. "I knew it!" he cried. "I knew you were that sort of man. When you entered my room, I said to myself, 'There stands a leader of men.' You will be good for Texas. I will help you."

"You are very kind."

"But you must swear to protect the Mexican government, and enter the Catholic church. Are you willing?"

Jim nodded. "I had understood those things. I am willing to uphold the Mexican government. And, although I was brought up a Presbyterian, I believe that every church has the same goal—toward God. I would feel privileged to become a member of your church."

"You must take instruction from our padre before the church will accept you."

"Of course."

Veramendi rose and Jim did also, believing this was his cue that the interview was over. However, the vice-governor motioned him to remain seated. He pulled a bell rope and a servant appeared.

"Señor Bowie will do us the honor of lunching with us," the vice-governor said. "Please see that a place is set for him."

"You are too kind." Jim was amused by Veramendi's imperious manner of announcing that he was eating with them, without first inviting him.

His word is law in this land, I see, Bowie said to himself. Soon a gong sounded and Veramendi led the way to a long dining room where even at midday candles glowed over smooth white damask and gleaming silver.

A handsome woman with dark hair slightly marked with silver stood at the doorway, her arm across the shoulders of a slim boy of about ten.

"Your son," Jim said to the vice-governor. "The resemblance is striking."

"*Si*. And my wife." The pride in the man's face was unmistakable. "*Querida,* may I present Señor James Bowie, a very great Americain? Señor Bowie, my wife Señora Maria Josefa Navarro Veramendi."

"It is our pleasure to have you dine with us," she said with charming grace.

"And this rascal is Carlos, my one and only son."

"Can I see your knife, Señor Bowie?" Carlos piped up.

"This is a friendly visit." Jim's eyes twinkled. "I came unarmed. Some other time, Carlos."

He heard high heels clicking on the hallway and turned to see two lovely girls enter the room.

"This is Teresa," Juan Veramendi said. "Our youngest daughter."

Jim guessed her age at about fourteen.

"And this, our elder daughter, is Urselita."

The girl raised her eyes and held out dainty finger tips to him. For a long moment while their eyes met, Jim's breath stopped. When she looked down quickly he realized that it was not the way for a Spanish maiden to give such a full glance to a man upon first acquaintance. Evidently she was as surprised by her boldness as he, for a flush spread over her olive skin. Creole women were famous for beauty, so he had not been starved in this respect. But this was the most beautiful girl Bowie had ever seen.

"Will you come this way," Señora Veramendi's gentle

voice brought Jim Bowie back to earth. "I insist that you sit at my right so that you two men will not talk politics during the whole meal. We would all like to share the attention of so distinguished and famous a gentleman."

Chapter Twelve

A YELLOW ROSE ON THE RIVERBANK

His acquaintanceship with the Veramendi family speedily opened doors for James Bowie, throwing him into a social whirl unrivaled in graciousness and luxury by any that he had experienced in Louisiana. The fine Spanish families of José Navarro, Señora Veramendi's parents, Francisco Ruiz, Juan Seguin, Placido Benavidos, the Flores, the De la Garzas were cultivated people who welcomed Bowie to their elaborate dinners and balls. Although he fitted easily into such a life, it was not for this he had come to Texas.

He threw himself vigorously into buying lands which seemed to promise a good investment and working with Juan Veramendi on plans to establish a textile mill. He also organized other energetic young Americans into a group which he called Rangers, but which the Mexicans called *Los Leonidas*—the Young Lions. The purpose of this organization was to discourage the raids of the Comanche on outlying ranches and settlements around Bexar. It took only a few counterraids by this vigorous, sharpshooting group to put a stop to the Indians' depredations.

It never ceased to surprise Jim to be pointed out as the "man who had invented the Bowie knife" and to see copies of the weapon in use wherever he went.

Now there was a song about it, sung everywhere:

"If you ever monkey with my Lulu gal,
I'll tell you what I'll do;
I'll carve you with my Bowie knife
And shoot you with my pistol, too."

Jim's lodgings were only a brief stroll from the Veramendi *palacio* and since he and the vice-governor had become partners in the textile mill project, it was natural that he was a frequent dinner guest at the Veramendi home. Soon he began to feel like one of the family. In the evenings after dinner it was extremely pleasant to sit or walk in the patio giving upon the willow-lined river.

As the lazy, pleasant days slid by, Jim was aware that the lovely Urselita was occupying his thoughts more and more. The picture of her beautiful eyes, her smooth olive skin, glossy black hair, the graceful movements of her hands, the quality of her voice were ever with him. He tried to push the thought of her away, telling himself that she was just a child—only eighteen to his thirty-five. How utterly absurd to be thinking of her so constantly, like a romantic schoolboy!

His plans were beginning to shape up well. He had purchased numerous tracts of land and was already recognized as a man of property and importance.

Now a new interest absorbed his attention. It was inevitable that he should hear tales of lost mines which have passed from generation to generation since the times of the early Spanish missions—stories of silver bars hidden in caves, of rich lodes lost to record because of the death, usually violent, of the key person who knew their location.

Several times Bowie was offered the opportunity to buy a "secret" map to some such treasure. He told Juan

Veramendi of such offers, but the vice-governor only scoffed. "Lost mines! Pouff!" he cried. "Don't waste time or thought on them!"

"But when the Lipan come to Bexar to trade," Bowie insisted, "they bring silver nuggets to buy goods with. Where does that come from?"

Veramendi shrugged. "Who knows? I do not doubt that silver exists back in the mountains. But white men could find it only at great peril. The Comanche will resist to the last man further invasion into their mountain fastnesses. Many others have attempted to find the lost mines. Most of them never return."

"No! No! Jaime!" Urselita's voice broke in with a shrill note of alarm. "Do not try to find the lost mines. It is too dangerous."

She had been sitting at the table silently listening to this talk and her sudden outburst caused everyone to stare at her in surprise. Tears filled her eyes. She put her hands to her cheeks to hide their telltale color and ran from the room.

Jim gave Don Juan a questioning look. He found a quizzical expression on the face of the vice-governor.

"I—I did not mean to offend her," Jim said lamely. "She seemed ready to burst into tears. Why?"

"I leave that for you to solve."

"But—but—!" Never had Jim Bowie been so at a loss for words. "She is only a child. It couldn't be that—that—"

"She is nearly nineteen," the vice-governor said gently. "Our girls mature early. She is a woman."

"But I am old enough to be her father. She is the most popular girl in Bexar. Surely she wouldn't be interested in me!"

"Who can fathom the heart of a young woman?" Doña Josefa murmured.

Jim rose suddenly and started to pace the floor. "Urselita's image has been in my heart from the moment I first saw her," he said. "She's the most beautiful—the loveliest person I've ever seen. I'm in love with her. But I didn't dare hope. . . ."

"When did Los Leoncitos not have the courage to dare try to win the heart of a woman? You, the bravest of men!" Veramendi's voice was tinged with amusement.

"But you? How do you and Doña Josefa feel about it? Would you favor my suit?"

Don Juan seemed to ponder the matter, but there was a twinkle in his eyes. "How about it, *querida,*" he finally said. "Would you favor Don Jaime as a son-in-law?"

She raised her large dark eyes and smiled. "Do not tease Don Jaime," she said. "You know we would both be most happy. But Urselita will have to decide for herself."

However, if Jim thought that the preliminaries to his courtship of Urselita Veramendi were settled he was to find himself very much mistaken. He found the girl elusive, even cool at times. At parties she seemed to avoid him and paid special attention to a handsome young Flores scion who had been courting her.

Jim began to believe that the Veramendis had been mistaken about their daughter's interest in him.

He joined the Catholic church, under the sponsorship of Veramendi, and so removed the religious obstacle, but Urselita remained aloof.

He went ahead trying to cultivate the friendship of the Lipan—the friendly Indians who came to San Antonio de Bexar to trade. He had managed to make slight headway with Chief Zolic, who always had a few nuggets of silver in a worn leather pouch tucked in his sash. Jim gave him a Bowie knife and so made an entering wedge into his friendship. Now Zolic looked him up when he came to trade.

There were no doubts in Bowie's mind that his future lay in Texas where opportunities were as vast as her acres. He made plans to return to Louisiana to dispose of his holdings there so that he could transfer his finances to his adopted home.

He was eager to get this over with for he had met an interesting character—Cephas Hamm, a hunter who had wandered far and wide throughout the Southwest.

"Once I went to live with a Lipan chief—just for the adventure of it," Cephas told Bowie. "A certain warrior often hunted with me. One time he pointed to a hill where he said there was a rich silver mine. I asked him to take me to it. He said that if we could manage to go hunting alone, he would, but that if the other Indians discovered what we were doing they would kill us both."

"Did you find the mine?" Jim asked eagerly.

Cephas shook his head. "Nope. The Lipan got into a fight with another tribe and my warrior friend was killed. I always intended to go looking on my own, but never got around to it."

"I must go back to Louisiana to wind up some business," Jim said. "Maybe when I get back we can go together."

"Maybe," Cephas agreed.

Jim was invited to dine with the Veramendis the evening before he was to leave for his old home. When Jim rose to make his farewells, he told the family how much he had enjoyed their hospitality.

"We will miss you," Doña Josefa said graciously.

"That we will," Don Juan agreed. "Don't forget to attend to all of the details of the textile mill."

"Oh, business! Business!" Doña Josefa broke in with what was for her exceptional impatience. "Have we not had enough of it? Urselita, that lovely pale yellow rose is in bloom at the river's edge. I am sure Don Jaime will want to see it before he leaves so that he can tell his friends in New Orleans what lovely roses we have here."

"I will be happy to show it to you, Jaime," the girl said demurely.

He walked beside her over the flagstone path. The yellow rosebush was conveniently located behind a willow. They could hear the voices of Don Juan and Doña Josefa not a stone's throw away, so they were properly chaperoned, yet out of sight.

Urselita cupped a perfect blossom in her graceful hands and her lovely head bent over it.

"It is beautiful." Jim's voice was husky and low. "But not nearly so beautiful as you, Urselita."

She raised her head and her great eyes stared into his. "Oh, Jaime!" she cried softly. "You are going away! Will you ever come back?"

"Do you want me to, Urselita?"

"If you don't, I would want to die." Her voice came in a half sob.

Then she was in his arms. When he raised his head from their first kiss he knew that never again would there be doubt in his heart. They loved each other truly and for all time. She was no child, but a woman, full blown as the rose at which they had just been looking.

"I will be back, Urselita," he promised, "bringing a ring to bind our troth."

"Hurry, Jaime. Please hurry!" she murmured.

Chapter Thirteen

JIM BOWIE MEETS SAM HOUSTON

Before Bowie set out to return to the Bayou Teche country he bought from Chief Zolic numerous gifts of silver to take to his family and friends. It was fall when he started. He rode by way of the Stephen Austin settlement of San Felipe on the Brazos. It would make a welcome break in his long journey, and he hoped to meet Austin who had made such a success of colonizing Texas.

At San Felipe, Jim stayed at the Peyton Tavern for several days, enjoying the rest and the company of these energetic Americans and their simple, easy-going way of life. These colonists, selected for their industry and integrity, had few comforts, but seemed not to mind the hardships. Most of them raised cattle, hogs, cotton and corn which they exported to Mexico or the States. Living mainly on salt pork, venison and corn pone, they got along with almost no cash, doing business by barter.

Jim went to call upon Stephen Austin, a tall, thin man, who worked hard and carried responsibility. He dealt with the central government at Mexico City and with his own state government at Saltillo. Both were as unstable as they were unpredictable. He was military and civilian chief to his colonists, besides being broker, banker, merchant and adviser in personal and business matters. And they were all completely devoted to him.

Jim's keen eyes took in the worn homespun suit, the lean body, the haggard, fine features. He told himself that here was a man unfitted by temperament to the hardships of frontier life. Bowie had heard that Austin liked the quiet pleasures of cultivated society, yet he was wearing himself to the bone carrying out the colonizing dream of his father Moses Austin, who had died before he himself could bring them to realization.

At the end of the brief visit, Jim said, "You are certainly to be congratulated upon your success in bringing civilization to this wilderness."

Jim returned to Arcadia and to bounteous southern hospitality.

Although his mother's hair was whiter and she seemed to have shrunk in size, she was still vigorous and spirited.

"What's this I hear about your selling out here and transferring all of your assets to Texas?" she asked, obviously not in favor of the idea.

Jim leaned forward in his chair and took her thin hands in his enormous strong ones. "It's true," he said. "There's something exciting about that country. It's a place of opportunity for the likes of me."

"But you're a gentleman," she protested. "Why should such a wild primitive land appeal to you?"

He smiled down on her fondly. "You were reared a lady—a gracious southern belle," he replied. "Yet you came here as a pioneer and fitted yourself into the harsh way of living and liked it."

Understanding came into her eyes. "I did like it," she said thoughtfully. "Perhaps because it was a challenge to my resourcefulness. But it was from your father that you inherited this wanderlust that is always driving you. Yet you fit in so beautifully with the gracious way of life that we helped establish in this region. When you first went to New Orleans and tasted this mode of living you couldn't rest until you made enough money to make it possible here."

"I still like it," he admitted. "But not as a steady diet. It's not exciting enough. But don't think that gracious living does not prevail in San Antonio de Bexar. The well-born Spanish people live every bit as luxuriously as we do on our plantation and in New Orleans and Natchez. They are cultivated, charming people—as you will see when I bring home Urselita, my beautiful bride-to-be."

Her eyes widened. "Jim!" she cried. "You aren't going to marry a Mexican girl?"

"Urselita de Veramendi is from an aristocratic Spanish family," he told her. "You'll love her. Wait and see."

"If she's the girl you've chosen for your wife, of course I'll love her." She smiled up at him.

Rezin was excited by what Jim told him about the lost mines of the Southwest. "If you find anything that looks promising, I'd like to join you on such an adventure," he cried eagerly.

Jim explained his plan of deliberately cultivating the friendship of the Lipan chief, hoping that he might gain some definite information. Rezin examined the beautiful silver belt Jim had brought him, his eyes alight with interest.

At Natchez Jim selected a rifle with elaborately engraved silver decorations to take back for a gift to Zolic.

"The old boy's claws will reach out to grab this." Jim told Rezin. "It should help me locate the famed San Saba mine. You can be sure that I'll send for you if anything exciting develops. Those southwestern mountains pull me. There's something about them—mystery, fascination."

"Not to speak of adventure—and the chance of a great fortune," Rezin added. "It would be fun to have one more topnotch adventure with you, Jim, before we settle down to being solid citizens for the rest of our lives."

"I'll try to work it out so that we can, Rez," Jim promised.

He went to Helena, Arkansas, to visit John and to dispose of his land holdings there. John had put on considerable weight and looked like the prosperous businessman he was. He was also a member of the legislature, and accustomed to being looked upon as a man of importance. But when it became known that Jim Bowie was in town, brother John played second fiddle. Men and boys crowded about to stare at Jim, and invariably they asked to see "the knife."

"Jim, you're famous!" John said. "I hope you don't get conceited."

"No danger." Jim's reply was abrupt. "I hope that I can someday do something which will be a more desirable claim to fame than being the originator of a symbol of bloodshed."

"You will," John assured him. "But the knife is more than a symbol of bloodshed. It's a symbol of man's right to protect himself against the heavy odds of a pioneer life. It's helping to carve civilization out of the wilderness."

"I hadn't thought of it that way," Jim said.

"Another thing you haven't thought of." John smiled. "You're a symbol yourself."

Jim looked surprised. "How do you mean?"

"Everyone loves a hero. You look like one. There's something about you, Jim. You stand out in any crowd. When you walk down the street people turn to look at you. Haven't you noticed?"

"Yes," Jim admitted. "And it bothers me. Makes me wonder if I look queer or forgot to put on my pants or something."

"It's because of a certain quality you have. That—and your reputation for utter fearlessness. Most men have to die before they gain such prominence."

"You're trying to inflate me." Jim laughed.

They strolled down to the boat landing on the Mississippi. Except for some Negroes loading cotton bales on a steamship docked at the wharf, no one was there. They were about to turn away when they saw a flatboat coming from up the river and waited for it to come to shore.

Two men leaned against the boat's cabin, staring at the town. One of them was bearded and it was he who drew Jim's eye. As the flatboat bumped against the wharf, he straightened up and Jim drew in his breath. The man was a giant! He wore the typical frontier garb—stained buckskin suit with fringes half gone and a wide-brimmed woolen hat. There was something about the set of his magnificent head which told him that here was a remarkable man.

"Sam!" John cried out. "Sam Houston. I didn't recognize you under all that foliage."

"Hello, John Bowie." The man's voice was deep enough to match his physical proportions.

He stepped ashore and shook John's hand. Immediately John introduced him to Jim.

Jim Bowie wasn't in the habit of looking up to many

men, being six feet, two himself, but Sam Houston towered over him.

"Jim Bowie," Houston said, gripping his hand. "I've heard of you. You're a legend, you know—you and your knife."

"I'm afraid that some of the reports you've heard were exaggerated," Jim said.

As they walked toward a tavern, Jim remembered what he had heard about this man. Once he had been the favorite of Andrew Jackson and had been governor of Tennessee. Later he had had the presidency of the United States practically in the palm of his hand. He had married the daughter of a prominent family, but within a few weeks he took her back to her father's home, resigned the governorship and disappeared into the wilderness to live among the Indians. He had become a man of mystery, but no one could forget his strange history. And Jim was certain he would never forget his strangely compelling personality, either.

Jim returned to Natchez to complete some business, then set off on horseback for Texas.

He reached San Antonio de Bexar just in time for the Christmas celebrations, of which the Mexicans made a great deal. He was all eagerness to see Urselita alone, but here he ran against the Spanish taboo in such matters. It was not proper for even engaged couples to be unchaperoned. Besides, there was all this uproar about the celebrations.

So Jim had to content himself with being part of the audience and enjoying the singing.

After the music the children broke into an excited clamor. "The *piñata!* The *piñata!*" they cried.

Jim had no idea what the word meant, but he soon

learned. Servants came in bearing a large, brightly colored clay jar in the form of a peacock. This was hoisted by a rope over a beam in the center of the ballroom. A child was blindfolded and handed a stick, then whirled around several times. He tried to strike the piñata with his stick. Each youngster was allowed three strikes, then he handed the stick to someone of his own choice who went through a similar performance. Every time someone missed, the rafters rang with shouts of delight from the spectators.

Finally the stick was passed to young Carlos de Veramendi. After he had been whirled around Jim saw him brace his sturdy legs, then stand still for a long moment as though to get his bearings. He struck twice and missed, but the third time he hit the piñata squarely. It broke and from it burst a shower of *dulces*—candies wrapped in bright paper. Then began an excited and noisy scramble, as each child fought for his share of the goodies.

This concluded the children's part of the performance. An orchestra moved into a corner of the long room where the grownups were to dance.

At once Urselita was surrounded by eager partners. Bowie's heart sank. He had not been quick enough, or could he bring himself to hurry in so undignified a manner. Yet he longed for a word with her. Then he saw her looking over the heads of the young men. Their eyes met, and Jim knew that hers were summoning him. Forgetting his precious dignity, he took long strides until he reached her side. "Our dance," he said and they glided over the floor in a quadrille.

She was feather light and graceful as a hummingbird

Dancing with her was sheer delight, but he wanted to speak to her alone.

"It has seemed so long," he whispered close to her ear.

"*Si.*" Her long eyelashes swept her cheeks.

"I must get you alone," he said.

"But no. It would be scandalous."

"We are engaged," he insisted. "Step into the garden with me. I must show you something."

"When the dance takes us near the door," she said.

Reaching the patio, Jim and Urselita strolled over to the place beneath the weeping willow tree, beside the yellow rose, where they had plighted their troth.

"Are you still sure, Urselita?" he asked.

"*Si!* Jaime. So sure."

He wanted to take her in his arms, but not so publicly.

"But you could have any man in Texas," he said. "I am older. I love you so dearly, Urselita. But I still can't believe that you really love me."

Soft laughter tinkled on her lips. "You are older. *Si.* But you make all the others seem such boys. Ah, Jaime. You do not see yourself as you are. When you come into the room—everything at once comes alive. The other men are pale—without character."

He drew from his pocket the ring he had purchased in Natchez and slipped it upon her finger. "In my country, this means that we are promised to each other for all time," he whispered. "Now please, darling, hurry the wedding date so that we can get away from this mob."

Chapter Fourteen

A TREASURE FOUND AND A TREASURE WON

Jim Bowie was to find that nothing could be rushed in Texas-Coahuila, especially the wedding of a daughter of a high-born Spanish family. Custom decreed that such arrangements should be very elaborate. Linens for numerous and varied uses must be embroidered, and it would take months to assemble a fitting trousseau for such a young lady. And during all this time the couple must never be unchaperoned.

Meanwhile Jim was building a fine home for his lovely Urselita, besides attending to the business details of installing the textile mill at Saltillo. Also, he was tracing to their sources the numerous fascinating tales of lost mines. The story which most interested him, because it obviously was based most firmly on fact, was about the lost San Saba mine.

Although not enthusiastic about his prospective son-in-law's interest in the subject, Don Juan made available to him the Miranda report, which sent Jim's adventurous blood coursing through his veins with excitement.

In 1756, according to the report, the governor of the province of Texas sent Lieutenant General de Miranda out with a small force to investigate the long persistent tales of a lost mine. He rode eight days to the northwest, setting up camp on the Arroyo San Miguel. Only a short distance ahead lay the Cerre del Almagre (Red Hill).

On the far side of this hill he came across a cave, which he named the Cave of St. Joseph of Alcasar.

Bowie read, "The mines are numerous. . . . The principal vein is more than two *varas* in width and in its westward lead appears to be of immeasurable thickness. . . . Fuel and water for mining operations are available near by."

The report further stated that Miranda, on his return to San Antonio de Bexar, met an Indian whom he trusted, who reported that more and richer mines were at Los Dos Almagres, close to the headwaters of the Colorado River. He said that his people were there to get solid silver with which to make *conchas* and other ornaments. Miranda offered his Indian friend a butcher knife and a red blanket to guide him there, but the Indian refused, saying that the Comanche were too numerous. They would all be tortured to death. "*Mañana*," he said, "I will lead you there, when the Comanche are far away."

Later on Jim learned the Mexican government had built a fort on the San Saba River. They had also established a mission three miles to the south. However, in 1758 the mission was overrun by two thousand Comanche and completely destroyed. The fort was so undermanned that it afforded little protection. Digging further into the records, Bowie found evidence that mining and smelting operations were carried on before the Indians drove the Mexicans from their diggings.

After reading the report Bowie waited impatiently for Zolic and his people to come to Bexar to trade. As the Veramendis had moved to their summer home in the mountains at Montaclava to escape the heat, Jim was more eager than ever for the chief to appear.

At last the Lipan came. Jim took the handsome silver-plated rifle and strolled casually down the street to the market place where the Lipan had spread out their wares.

He found old Zolic dozing in the shade of a pecan tree and quietly sat down beside him. The chief opened his eyes.

"*Hola,*" Jim said.

He suppressed a grin at the way the Indian looked at the weapon lying across his lap. He saw the talonlike fingers curl and uncurl as if he could scarcely keep from grabbing it.

"*Buena.* Good gun," Zolic said finally.

"Yes, it is," Bowie drawled. "The finest rifle I've ever handled. Want to look at it?" He laid the gleaming weapon in Zolic's lap.

The chief examined it from every angle, stroking the muzzle, eying the exquisite silver mounting.

"Will give you blanket, hides for it," he said. Although he tried to speak casually, there was a greedy gleam in the Indian's eyes.

"No," Jim said.

"Two blankets. Much silver."

Jim shook his head.

"Much, much silver—*conchas,* belts, bracelets."

"No," Jim repeated. "The rifle is not for trade. I brought it to you as a gift, because you are my brother."

"You give to me?" His tone was incredulous.

"Yes, my brother."

"I will give you gift in exchange. It is the Lipan way."

Bowie shook his head. "No. I would like to hunt with you, my brother."

The old chief nodded slowly. "*Buena.* You will come

to my camp. Live in my lodge. We are brothers. Will hunt together."

Three days later Jim Bowie and Zolic rode side by side toward the mysterious blue mountains. It was late evening when they reached the Lipan village. As they rode in they were surrounded by warriors who gave the visitor frowning scrutiny, but when Zolic spoke to them their frowns vanished.

Jim was led into the chief's lodge—the largest in the village.

While he lived among the Lipan, Jim became one of them as much as possible. He ate the dog stew and other concoctions they enjoyed, learned to shoot the bow and arrow as skillfully as any brave, taught them how to throw the Bowie knife. Soon his skin took on an Indian copper color, although his gray-blue eyes and red hair set him apart from the others. The Lipan called him *Cuchillo Grande*, Big Knife.

Every day when they went out to hunt, Jim kept his eyes open, but took care not to excite suspicion. He was looking for a red hill. It was nearly time for him to return to Bexar before he saw it one day when he and Zolic were hunting far from camp. He had shot and wounded a deer which disappeared over a rise. Jim put his horse to the gallop trying to overtake the wounded animal. At last he brought it down near a clump of brush.

He rode over and drew his knife to slit its throat. He was straightening up when something strange about the appearance of the area behind the bushes caused him to pull some branches aside. He caught his breath. Here was a well-concealed cave! He entered the cave and when his eyes grew accustomed to the dim light he saw stacks of bar silver and chunks of loose nuggets on the ground.

Stepping outside he started dressing the deer, but while he worked he made mental notes of the landmarks. He saw that this hill was definitely reddish in color. Near by were the ruins of a stone wall and close to it was a large slab with a trace of silver sticking to it. His heart beat fast. He had discovered the lost San Saba mine! Would his luck hold, now that great treasure was within his grasp? There had been many others who had come far only to fail in the end.

He heard hoofbeats. Zolic was riding up. Jim knelt beside the deer with his back to the bushes which concealed the cave. He looked up and grinned. "I almost lost this buck," he said. "But I finally brought him down. I must practice my marksmanship more."

Zolic looked at him with a trace of suspicion, but Jim acted innocent. He hated to deceive this fine man who had befriended him, but he realized it would be better if Zolic did not know that he had discovered the silver. Then the chief could always truthfully tell his tribesmen that he had not led *Cuchillo Grande* to it.

They loaded the deer carcass onto the pack horse, and rode silently to camp.

Bowie managed to restrain his impatience to return to Bexar, now that he had found what he was looking for. He stayed another week in camp, then left for San Antonio to make ready for his approaching marriage.

The bells of San Fernado Parish Church rang out a vibrant summons. Jim Bowie had heard them hundreds of times, but now their clanging was summoning him to his wedding. He was dressed in a new dark broadcloth suit with a dove-colored brocaded vest and wide flowing black tie. His shirt was of finest linen and his shoes, polished to reflect like a mirror, were of glove-soft leather. He moistened his dry lips nervously, then squared his shoulders and made his way to the church across the square. Carriages lined the streets as far as he could see. Well-dressed men and their mantilla-draped wives were entering the church. The thought of facing all those people and of the elaborate Catholic marriage ceremony gave him stage fright.

But when he stood before the altar and saw Urselita coming up the aisle on the arm of her father, all his panic evaporated. She wore a dress of creamy satin and her face was veiled. But through the veil he saw that beloved face, those madonnalike eyes radiant, and his heart was filled with an overwhelming joy.

After the wedding there was a reception at the Veramendi *palacio,* with the inevitable feasting and dancing which lasted three days. Then finally the young couple were allowed to go to their own home.

In a week they set out in a carriage for the Bayou Teche country.

* * *

Elvira Bowie looked at her new daughter-in-law for a long moment, then took her in her arms. "She is even lovelier than you said," his mother remarked over the bride's shoulder. "I love her dearly."

Jim nearly burst with pride over Urselita's social success. Her beauty and charm won every heart. And even in this land famed for beautiful and charming women, she stood out like some rare, exotic flower.

Jim took her to New Orleans where he looked up his

old friend James Audubon, now famous since the publication of his book of bird paintings.

"I know that you'd rather paint portraits of birds than of people," Jim said. "But as a special favor I'd like to have you paint a portrait of my lovely Urselita."

"This commission will be a joy," Audubon said. "If I could always paint such beauty in human face and form, I might forsake my precious birds. Hers is beauty not just on the surface. It comes from a lovely soul within."

"I want my Jaime's portrait painted, too," Urselita insisted.

"Oh, no!" Jim protested. "Audubon is a very great artist and he is particular about his subjects."

Audubon shrugged. "I will paint my friend James also—because his lovely bride wishes me to. But I could be better employed out in the swamps." His eyes twinkled at Jim.

Chapter Fifteen

TREASURE HUNT

Before Jim and Urselita returned to Texas, he told Rezin all about his finding evidence of the old mine. So Rez made plans to join his brother in November.

By the time Rezin reached San Antonio de Bexar, Jim had won Urselita's consent to his setting out to search for the mine on the San Saba. At first she had raised a great outcry about the danger of such a venture.

Jim had laughed at her fears. "Give Rezin and me a handful of Texans," he scoffed, "and we'll be the match of any Indians we meet."

"But the Comanche are so fierce—so cruel," she cried.

But when she saw his jaw set, she said, "The saints will protect you. You love the spice of danger. I love you for what you are. I would not change you."

When news of the project leaked out the members of Los Leoncitos clamored to go. Rezin was in favor of a strong force. Jim, however, said a handful of men could travel and maneuver much faster. So, besides the two leaders and their two servants, only seven men were picked for the treasure hunt, one of whom was Cephas Hamm.

Bowie led his small force over much the same route as Zolic had taken him. Later he would branch off toward the Red Hill.

He told the men that the ruins of an old fort lay about thirty miles ahead on the San Saba River. They should be able to reach it by nightfall and it would afford good protection in case a battle with any Indians developed. The route was so crisscrossed by rocky arroyos that the horses' hoofs were badly damaged and they found it impossible to reach the fort that night.

Jim had picked a place to set up camp on a slight elevation where a small timber island of about thirty live oaks grew. On the northern rim was a thicket of bushes and below was a stream of running water.

Everything we need, Jim thought.

The men cleared the prickly pear from the thicket, making a circle where the horses could be hobbled. A trail was slashed through to the stream. Guards were placed for the night.

Morning dawned clear and calm. Cephas Hamm climbed the tallest tree and looked over the country but reported that he saw no signs of any Indians.

"The fort is only about six miles farther on," Jim said. "It will be better protection if Indians do strike. And we'll be that much nearer our goal."

Since many of the horses had gone lame it was necessary to rearrange the supplies, so it was nearly eight o'clock when they were ready to set out.

Cephas climbed his tree for another look. He came scrambling down quickly. "Injuns to the east!" he cried. "One of 'em has his face to the ground as if he was sniffing our trail."

"Dismount! Prepare for defense!" Jim's voice snapped.

The saddle and pack horses were tethered. The men stationed themselves behind the trunks of the largest trees. Soon bloodcurdling war whoops split the air. The Indians could be seen stripping and then daubing war paint on their bodies.

A man named Buchanan, who knew a smattering of Caddo, offered to go out and parley with the Indians if someone would accompany him.

"I know a bit of Indian," Jim said. "I'll go. Keep us covered, Rez. Since they are about a hundred and sixty-four to our eleven I hope we can talk them out of fighting."

The two men strode forward boldly.

"Send out your chief," Buchanan shouted in Caddo. "We want to talk to him."

"Howdy do! Howdy do!" the Indians replied. Evidently this was the extent of their English.

Their next greeting was a barrage of shot, one of which broke Buchanan's leg. Jim returned their fire with a double-barreled shotgun and a pistol. Then he reached down and lifted Buchanan over his shoulder.

As he staggered back toward the encampment he was surrounded by heavy fire. Two more shots hit Buchanan. Seeing that their gunfire did not bring down Jim Bowie, eight warriors came at him with upraised tomahawks. But Rezin and several others rushed to Jim's rescue and sent the Indians running, after killing four of them. Buchanan was laid in the shade of a tree where Rezin dressed his wounds.

The men discovered that a hill to the northeast, about sixty yards away, was swarming with Indians. They began a heavy fire accompanied by shrill war whoops. Their chief was at the front, urging his men to charge.

"Get that Indian on horseback. He's the chief," Jim shouted.

Several shots were fired and he was brought down. His warriors rushed forward to carry him from the battlefield, and then went over the hill out of sight, giving the white men a chance to reload.

Soon the Indians reappeared firing bows and arrows. The Texans took deadly aim with their rifles. Now another chief began haranguing his warriors.

Jim aimed, fired and the second chief fell to the ground. He, too, was caught up by his men and carried off.

"If we keep picking off their chiefs we'll soon have them plumb discouraged." Cephas Hamm laughed.

"We must plan better, though," Jim said, "so every shot will count. Only five men fire at one time. Then there will always be five guns loaded."

While the attention of the treasure seekers was taken up by the attack from the Indians on the hill, twenty of the Caddo crept under the bank at the rear and opened fire. Soon the Indians had completely encircled Bowie's handful of men, concealing themselves behind the shrubbery.

"We're too exposed," Jim shouted. "To the bushes, men."

Crouching low, the Bowie men scampered into the bushes in which the small clearing had been made. Although they were not as well protected as they had been by the oak trunks, the men had an advantage here, for they could see the enemy without being seen.

"Move every time you fire," Bowie ordered.

This strategy proved sound, for the Indians' only target was the smoke from the rifles. For two long hours the fighting went on with only one other Bowie man being wounded. The Indians on the other hand were losing heavily from the deadly aim of the Texans.

Now the Indians adopted a more dangerous tactic.

They set fire to the dry grass which lay near the Bowie camp, and under cover of the smoke were able to carry off their dead and wounded. The wind from the west whipped the fire into black billows of smoke from which darted forked tongues of flame. The grass shriveled, then leaped into blaze. The white men were gasping and choking and could not see their enemy.

Behind the curtain of smoke the Indians whooped as though already celebrating a victory.

"Work, boys, work!" Jim shouted, himself a fury of energy as he piled rocks for a breastwork, scraped dead grass from around the wounded and beat out creeping flames with blankets.

It was like the inside of a furnace. Sparks filled the air and fell on their faces. But they beat the licking flames and labored with knives or bare hands to heighten the breastwork and dig a trench. Outside the ring of fire the Indians kept up their incessant whooping and yelling.

"The red devils must think we're already roasting at the stake," Jim growled as he and Rezin worked shoulder to shoulder.

Then the flames ran into bare ground and died on one side of the camp and on the other side the fire was checked by the stream.

Having failed to burn the white men out, the Indians again occupied the point of rocks and began a fierce attack. The wind veered, blowing strongly from the north. Jim bade the two servants scrape away the dry leaves and grass from their side of the encampment. It was too much to hope that the redskins would fail to notice the advantage this change in wind direction gave them.

Soon one of them was seen crawling to the creek with

a firebrand in his hand. He managed to fire the grass on the side near the camp and shortly the flames, ten feet high, raced toward the white men.

Should they remain in this spot and be cooked or go out onto the prairie where they would certainly fall into the hands of the Indians?

The men gathered about Bowie. "Keep your powder horns closed," he ordered, "or we'll be blown to bits. We each have one load apiece to use on the red devils. When they charge, let them have it. Then we'll stand back to back and use our knives as long as possible. We must all fight the fire with buffalo robes, deerskins and blankets, and protect our wounded."

As the brush burned, the circle became smaller and smaller. But evidently the flames were too hot for the Indians, so the men had time to build their breastwork higher and dig a trench with knives and sticks.

With the setting of the sun, the clamor around the camp died down, as did the wind. The fire died, too, when it reached the ground which the trapped men had scraped bare.

They had been fighting furiously since sunrise, and now that the battle was over they realized how exhausted they were. The Indians withdrew beyond rifle fire and set up a mournful wailing over their dead.

But the Bowie men did not waste time. They buried the one man who had been killed and attended to the three wounded as best they could. They filled their canteens, cups and cooking pans with water and soaked the blankets in case the fire broke out again. Then they worked feverishly until long into the night, raising and strengthening the breastwork, getting ready for the attack all were sure would come with the dawn.

However, the expected attack did not develop. When it was light enough to see, Bowie peered toward the hill where the Indians had been camped, but they had vanished. Later Jim and Cephas Hamm rode out to reconnoiter. They counted forty-eight telltale red spots on the ground. Three of those killed had been chiefs.

"It's sure as the sun shines that a third of their number was wiped out," Cephas said triumphantly. "I believe they're plumb discouraged with fighting an outfit like ours."

"I hope they stay discouraged," Jim said.

They did. The white men remained in the comparative safety of their little fortress for eight days, waiting for the wounded men and horses to recover sufficiently to be moved—and to see if the Indians showed any further inclination to fight.

Jim and Rezin did not know then that this fight was to go down in history as the fiercest ever recorded in Indian warfare. They were not much concerned with their historic battle. They were heartsick that their treasure hunt had failed.

"We'll try again, won't we, Jim?" Rez said as they were riding back toward Bexar.

"Of course," his brother said confidently. "As soon as we can reorganize."

But when he reached home Urselita had news for him which changed his mind.

"I'm sorry, Rez," he said. "We'll have to postpone our plans—perhaps until next fall. You see," his chest swelled, "I'm going to be a father. I couldn't leave Urselita now."

Chapter Sixteen

STORM CLOUDS GATHERING

News of the extraordinary victory at San Saba against the Indians added to the growing prestige of James Bowie.

Now the Bowie knife was the preferred weapon of all frontiersmen. Powder and lead were expensive, and precious time was lost in reloading after each shot. But the Bowie knife was always ready for quick action and a dozen uses.

Many of these knives were manufactured in England. There was some variation in both the length and breadth of the blade, but otherwise the weapons were nearly exact copies of the original one made by James Black.

Many of Jim's friends tried in vain to pry from him the location of the San Saba mine, but he refused to disclose the secret.

Although plans for another treasure hunt were still very active in his mind, Jim's main interest was in Urselita and their coming child.

Usually restless to be on the go, Jim now resented the need to travel back and forth to Saltillo and other places to attend to the many business affairs in which he and his father-in-law were involved. He was afraid he might be absent at the time of the child's birth.

However, he was at home when it took place. But he found himself reduced to maddening uselessness when

Doña Josefa took affairs in her capable hands and shooed Jim from the room.

"This is no place for a man," she said firmly. "You're in the way.

At last Doña Josefa called him inside and placed in his arms a blanket-wrapped bundle.

"Your daughter," Doña Josefa said proudly.

For the first time in his life Jim Bowie wanted to remain at home, but the press of business and events made it more imperative than ever that he spend most of his days in the saddle.

Political affairs were now in such a ferment that Don Juan's constant presence at his desk in Bexar was required. So Jim had to ride back and forth to Saltillo to keep the steam factory for manufacturing cotton goods running smoothly. He and Veramendi were also involved in numerous real estate deals. Then, too, as Bowie had become an important person in Texas, he was expected to assume heavy responsibilities during this critical time.

A new president, Bustamante, had risen to power, and immediately trouble began. He promptly forbade further immigration from the United States, imposed heavy taxes and duties on the colonists and decreed that from now on Texas was to be colonized only by Mexicans who would also administer all affairs.

There were feelings of ill will on both sides. The well-founded rumor that the American government planned to annex Texas—had, in fact, offered to buy the province for one million dollars—alarmed Mexico. Some American statesmen considered that by the terms of the Louisiana Purchase, Texas belonged to the United States. The colonists, in turn, feared that they might lose the holdings for which they had labored so hard.

Austin called a convention to meet in October, 1832, at San Felipe, to discuss the new crisis and to ask for greater liberties under the Mexican law. Of course Jim Bowie was there. But Mexico City completely ignored the resolutions passed at the meeting. As the Bustamente regime grew more harsh, trouble-breeding incidents between the colonists and the Mexicans increased.

The following year Austin called for another convention to meet in December.

"You don't have to go this time, Jaime!" Urselita protested when she heard her father and husband discussing the matter.

"Of course he must go, *muchacha,*" Don Juan said. "Don Jaime is an important man. His words bear weight in such meetings."

"But it will mean that he will be away from us during the Nativity celebrations," she said.

Bowie drew her close. "I always suffer when I am away from you, *querida,*" he said tenderly, "and it will be worse to be separated from you and the baby during the Christmas season. Perhaps we can get the convention over quickly so I can be with you."

She shook her head. "You men with your tiresome politics! You talk, talk, talk—and get nowhere."

Jim chuckled. "We should be stingy with words, as the women are, eh? You may depend upon it, *novia,* I shall be back with you as soon as possible."

Arriving at San Felipe de Austin, Bowie sought lodging at Peyton Tavern. When he entered the long room he saw a giant of a man standing before the great fireplace. There was something familiar about the set of the magnificent head on those massive shoulders. Then, as though drawn by Bowie's stare, the man turned and his stern features broke into a smile of welcome.

"Jim Bowie!" he cried, seizing Jim's hand in a bone-crushing grip. "How lucky to run into you!"

At first Jim did not recognize this man who was so vastly changed since their chance meeting at the river landing in Arkansas. Now he was clean shaven save for the bushy sideburns, and his clothing was well tailored.

"Sam Houston!" Jim cried. "I didn't expect to find you here."

Houston grinned. "President Jackson sent me with a message to Steve Austin. But I reckon I would've come anyway. Seems as if things are about to pop wide open here in Texas—and Sam Houston's the man to be in the middle of any scrap."

"We must be kindred spirits, suh," Bowie remarked. "I used to tell my brother Rezin that I aimed to live to the hilt during my prime, then go out in a blaze of glory."

These two men, both giants in stature as well as spirit, stood measuring each other. It seemed as though this was a fateful moment—that these two natural leaders of men had come together for a special purpose.

The convention of 1833 proposed a state constitution and asked for separation from the Mexican state of Coahuila, with free immigration and some minor reforms. It denied any wish for independence.

Word came from Mexico City that Santa Anna had overthrown Bustamente. The Texans were sure that the new president would be friendly to their cause, and

Stephen Austin volunteered to carry their message in person to the Mexican capital.

There was an air of jubilance among the settlers when the convention was adjourned. They believed that their problems were over.

Bowie and Houston, who had become well acquainted during the meetings, drew together at their close.

Bowie sighed. "I had hoped to be with my family on Christmas Day. What do you say we dine here together, suh? You say you plan to ride to Bexar. I should be proud to have you as my guest there, but I suppose that my father-in-law will snatch you from me."

"I'll enjoy riding with you," Houston said. "I'd planned to talk to Veramendi. You can bring me up to date on Texas affairs as we travel."

Jim longed to be with Urselita, enjoying the special celebration the Veramendis made of Christmas. He therefore welcomed the company of Sam Houston, a fascinating conversationalist and good companion.

One thing, though, which Houston told him made Jim shudder. Bowie had mentioned that he might have to make a business trip back to the States the following summer.

"I trust," Houston said, "the plague will have run its course by then."

"What plague?"

"Asiatic cholera. An epidemic has been raging through the whole Mississippi Valley. It was probably brought in by some sailor from the Black Sea. In New Orleans alone, five thousand have died in less than two weeks. Doctors work day and night until they themselves lie down to die. Bodies are piled like corkwood and buried in great trenches. It has spread upriver to all the towns.

Fur traders carried it to the Indians and whole tribes were wiped out."

Jim's face had turned pale. He thought of his family back in Louisiana and his loved ones here in Texas. "We heard nothing of the pestilence here," he said. "I pray that it doesn't strike this part of the country."

"Texas is too sparsely settled for it to take hold here," Houston's words were faintly reassuring.

While they ate a well-cooked Christmas dinner, Jim told Houston of the factors which had brought about the present crisis in Texas.

"As you probably know, suh, the trouble started in 1830 when Mexico passed a law checking further immigration into Texas."

Houston nodded.

Jim went on. "There was fault on both sides, I reckon. The Bustamante regime has been too harsh for the high-spirited Texans. We look for an improvement now that Santa Anna is in power. And naturally Mexico grew alarmed over the zeal of the United States government to buy Texas.

"But the biggest trouble," Jim added seriously, "arose when Bradburn—a Kentuckian, mind you, but in the paid service of the Mexicans—arrested William Travis and other Anglo-Americans on some trivial charge. Of course the Texans would not stand for that and one hundred and sixty armed colonists marched to Anáhuac to their rescue. Travis and the others were soon freed, but there was a fierce, short battle at Velasco. A small Mexican force surrendered there, but were released upon their promise that they would not again attack Texans."

"General Jackson wonders if Travis' friends did not go too far," Houston said thoughtfully.

"Some of the colonists think so, too. This little incident, trivial as it may seem, might be the tinder to set off a real explosion in Texas affairs."

"It's often little things like that which start big wars," Houston said sagely.

Next day they set out for San Antonio de Bexar. As soon as they arrived Jim introduced Houston to Vice-president de Veramendi. Although his father-in-law seemed to regard Don Samuel, as he called Houston, with some suspicion, he insisted that Houston be his guest during his stay in Bexar.

Jim, too, thought there was some mystery connected with Houston's presence in Texas. The matter was somewhat clarified just before Houston was to return to Nacogdoches, Texas.

As they were talking together, Houston suddenly threw out a challenging remark, "How do you stand on the Texas question, Jim?"

"What do you mean?"

"Like the other Texans, you became a Mexican citizen in order to hold lands here. By marriage you're tied to the highest in the Mexican government. But you're American born. If it comes to a showdown of Texans' fighting for independence, where will you stand?"

"Suh, I consider your question premature!"

"And impertinent?" Sam threw in with a laugh. "Forgive me, Jim. That was a very personal question and you've a right to resent it. Yet I've reasons for asking. You're a leader—will be whichever side you're on."

"Whatever influence I may have," Jim said stiffly, "I am trying to use to avert trouble among my people, both Mexican and American."

Houston nodded understandingly. "And you're doing a good job of it. Yet I'm afraid the fat's in the fire. Because I consider you my friend, I'm going to confide in you. But I ask you to keep this matter between us. Here's a report I'm sending to my president from Nacogdoches as soon as I get there."

He handed a paper to Jim.

Bowie read the communication addressed to General Jackson, in which Houston reported that nineteen twentieths of the population of Texas wanted the United States to acquire the province; that Mexico was involved in civil war; that the people of Texas were determined to form a state government; and that Mexico's want of money, taken in connection with the course which Texas "*must* and *will* adopt" would render a transfer of Texas to some power inevitable.

He concluded with these words: "My opinion is that Texas, by her members in convention, will, by the first of April, declare all that country (north of the Rio Grande) as Texas proper, and form a state constitution. I expect to be present at that convention, and will apprise you of the course adopted. I may make Texas my abiding place, but I will never forget the country of my birth." The letter was signed, "Your friend and obedient servant, Sam Houston."

Jim handed the document back to Houston. "I believe, suh, that you've summed the matter up very neatly. And if so, as you said, the fat *is* in the fire. Perhaps you have a better perspective on affairs than we have who are so close to it."

"I think so," Houston answered. "And if a crisis comes, as I'm sure it must, be sure, Jim Bowie, that you're on the side of right. For you're a big man, and we'll need you."

"When the time comes—if it does—I'll let my conscience be my guide," Jim said, holding out his hand to bid his strangely fascinating friend farewell.

Chapter Seventeen

HEARTBREAK

Bowie's divided loyalties did not prove to be as troublesome as he had feared. Most of the highborn Mexicans to whom he was tied by marriage or friendship were as fervently against the oppressive rule of Bustamante as were the colonists. When it was learned that the hated president had been overthrown by Santa Anna, Texans and Mexicans alike cheered, believing that the crisis in Texas affairs had passed safely.

Yet when month after month went by and Stephen Austin did not return, the colonists grew suspicious. It was rumored that Austin had been thrown into prison, but no one knew if this were true.

Meantime Jim Bowie had other matters to worry about. He received a frantic letter from Maggie, Rezin's wife, saying that his brother was going blind. Could Jim come and take care of his business matters?

"No! No!" Urselita clung to him. "The plague! The terrible plague. I will not allow you to go where it is raging."

"But I must go, *mi querida*. Rezin is my other self. He needs me."

Urselita's beautiful dark eyes flashed. "But what about me? I am your wife. It is *I* who is your other self. You know that I am with child again. I need you, too."

Jim took her in his arms tenderly. "Try to understand," he said gently. "You are my wife—my very soul, closer than my other self. But you will be here with your family. You will be cared for. At the moment Rezin's need for me is greater. I must see that he has the best doctors. He's a brilliant man. It's unthinkable that he should spend the rest of his days in darkness. I will not let it happen. I'll sell Arcadia and see that he and his family and my mother are comfortably settled in a smaller place. And I shall hurry back to you, *novia*. I shall be here before our child is born."

"Then go," she said with a sigh. "I would not be so selfish as to hold you—but take care of yourself—my beloved. *Voya con Dios!*"

Three times Rezin had represented his parish in the state legislature, greatly distinguishing himself. Jim was determined that his brother's career should not be blighted by blindness.

Jim found Rezin's condition as serious as Maggie had said. He promptly took his brother to Baltimore where the best eye specialist in the country practiced. Later Jim left Rezin there for treatment while he returned to Louisiana to sell his brother's widely scattered lands.

The work of disposing of Rezin's land holdings could not be done hurriedly. So it was October before Jim was free to set out for home—and the child had been expected in September. He would make Urselita understand, for she was the kindest, most unselfish of women.

Before he left Jim saw Rezin and his family and his mother comfortably established in a lovely home in Avoyelles Parish.

Gripping Rezin's hand at parting, Jim said, huskily, "Take care of yourself now, Rez. Get those eyes well so we can have another go at our silver mine."

"I'm planning on it." Rezin smiled. "I hope to make it next spring."

"I'll have all the arrangements made. You'd better bring Mom and Maggie and the girls. I want them to meet my children. There are two of them by now. And I haven't even met my son yet."

"That's a long, hard journey for an old lady," Elvie said. "Better bring your family here."

"You're as spry as any girl of twenty," he told her.

Jim took with him a sturdy Negro named Ham as his servant. As he rode the long miles through forests and plains, fording wild rivers, sleeping under the stars, he dreamed of San Antonio de Bexar drowsing in the sun, and of his own home where Urselita would welcome him, her madonnalike eyes full of love. Now she would be holding the new baby.

Finally they reached San Felipe. When Jim, exhausted by the journey, stumbled into Peyton Tavern the proprietor stared at him strangely.

"What's the matter?" Jim asked a trifle testily.

"Nothing at present. Eat your supper. Then I have news for you."

"Tell me now. I insist."

"No." Mr. Peyton shook his head. "I can see you're worn out. You need food. Meet me in my office after you've eaten."

Jim shrugged. Probably the news had something to do with Texas politics. At the moment he did not want to hear about it, for he was dead tired. He wanted to eat, fall into bed, then set out at dawn for home.

The meal made him more drowsy than ever. He was tempted to pass the office and go straight to his room, but Mr. Peyton was waiting by the door and beckoned to him.

With a yawn Jim sank into a chair.

"Brace yourself, Mr. Bowie," the innkeeper said. "I have bad news. You've probably heard that the cholera has taken heavy toll in Texas?"

Jim gasped. His heart stopped beating for a moment. "My family? Not Urselita or the child."

Peyton nodded.

"Which one? Not both of them. For God's sake, man, tell me!"

"I have a letter here from your brother-in-law. You'd better read it."

Jim rose to his feet. "Tell me what it says. Quickly!"

"When the cholera hit Bexar," Peyton said, "Veramendi fled with his family, including your wife, little daughter and your newborn son, to his mountain home in Montaclava. But it was too late. Veramendi—every member of your family and his died of the plague."

A roar of anguish came from Jim Bowie's throat. "It can't be!" he cried. "I don't believe it. What hideous lie are you telling?"

"It is true. I am more sorry than I can say."

Jim seized the letter, read and reread the terrible news. "Then it's true," he moaned. "It is Navarro's writing. What have I done to deserve this?"

He stumbled from the office. Loungers in the tavern stared at him—frightened at the wild look in his eyes.

"Call my boy Ham," Bowie cried in a hoarse voice. "Tell him to saddle the horses."

"You're not setting out tonight, I hope," Mr. Peyton said. "You're exhausted. It's storming."

"How could I rest?" Bowie whirled on him. "How can

I ever rest? My Urselita gone! My daughter! The son I never saw. . . ."

Sobs choked him. He staggered from the tavern, out into the night where strong wind and cold, drenching rain beat upon him.

Jim Bowie did not want to go on living. Existence had lost all meaning for him. He could not bear to go back to the home where Urselita had always run to meet him with a smile of joy and where his little daughter had toddled toward him with outstretched arms. He stayed at an inn and roamed the streets aimlessly, trying to find relief for the grief which was devouring him.

He blamed himself. Perhaps if he had not gone to Louisiana, this terrible thing might not have happened. Oh, if only he could have died with his loved ones!

He went back to his family in Louisiana, hoping to find relief, but decided he was more miserable there than in Texas. Rezin's condition was somewhat improved. There was no business with which Jim could occupy himself. The days dragged unbearably.

"I reckon I'll be better off in Texas," he finally told his mother. "Things are going bad for the colonists. I can be useful there."

Mrs. Bowie nodded. "I think you're wise," she said. "Lock this sorrow in your heart. Throw your great energies into some work or some cause. You'll be happier."

"I can never be happy again," he said bitterly.

"You can at least be useful." There was a snap to her voice and in her eyes. "No son of mine will sit back and feel sorry for himself. There's no use blaming yourself. You couldn't have held off the plague from hitting your loved ones if you'd been there."

"I could have died with them then."

"But you didn't. You're alive and must keep on living and carrying your weight in the world. Perhaps fate had a hand in this. You know"—her eyes took on a strange, faraway look—"I've always had a feeling about you. That destiny had singled you out for a special purpose. Few men get to be legends during their lifetime."

"Because of a bloodstained knife! What a road to glory!"

"Stop being bitter. Get hold of yourself. Go out with head up to meet whatever lies in your path."

For the first time in months a smile quirked at his lips. "You're good for me, Mother Elvie," he said patting her shoulder. "I'll brace up and take anything life hands me without crying."

"That sounds like my son," she said proudly.

When Ham brought around the horses Rezin clasped Jim's hand and said, "Get ready for that treasure hunt. As soon as my eyes are better I'll come out to join you."

"I'll be waiting," Jim responded, although he now had no interest in the silver mine. Of what use was wealth to a man without a family?

Chapter Eighteen

TENSE TIMES

Back in San Antonio, Bowie tried to take up the broken threads of his life. He put the big white house up for sale and also sold his interest in the textile mill in Saltillo.

He found the political affairs of Texas still as unsettled as when he had left. The fact that nothing had been heard from Stephen Austin did not ease the strained relations between the colonists and Mexico.

The Texans had hoped that with the reins of government in the hands of Santa Anna restrictions would be eased, but so far nothing like that had happened.

Jim Bowie went back to dealing in land. He had brought a number of commissions from Louisiana friends who wished to speculate in Texas real estate. Although he made a nice profit on these transactions, he had little interest in money.

That spring the people in San Antonio were talking about a new development in Texas political affairs. Usually the Mexican government kept only a small garrison at Bexar, but suddenly Colonel Domingo de Ugartecha, the new commandant, had brought his military up to over four hundred men. Added to that came a rumor that Santa Anna was about to march upon Texas with strong military forces. The new dictator had given himself the title, "Napoleon of the West."

Upon hearing this Bowie said to his friends, "Santa

Anna is proving himself an even worse tyrant than Bustamante."

The news spread rapidly, and almost as speedily Texas split into two factions, the War party and the Peace party, with constant bickering between them. As the Mexican custom laws became more strict and the troops more arrogant and overbearing, the War party grew in strength and more and more talk about Texas independence was heard.

Bowie did not join in this futile quarreling, but he longed for some action which would take his mind from his tragic loss. He rode to Matamoros, the great Mexican port at the mouth of the Rio Grande, to do a little private spying. Although he was dressed as a Mexican and could speak the language fluently, there was little he could do to disguise his red hair and blue eyes, except keep his wide hat pulled low to shade his face.

No particular spying was necessary to sense war in the air, however. Matamoros, usually a sleepy town, was now bustling with activity. Over the cobbled streets strode *zapadores,* dragoons and lancers, dressed in new uniforms.

Bowie slipped in and out of the smoky *cantinas* and heard the loud boasts of the coming expedition to subdue the Texans. More important, he discovered that every sort of craft in the river's mouth was being made ready to transport troops.

He had felt fairly safe until the second day when he saw signs posted on the walls forbidding all foreigners to leave the city.

After nightfall he slipped out of town and quietly rode away. When he was far enough from the city, he set his horse to a gallop and rode all night, hiding in groves of trees during the day. He traveled up the Texas coast until he arrived at Hatch's Plantation on the Lavaca River. From there he promptly dispatched a letter to the political chief of the Brazos department, reporting about the vessels at Matamoros and of the orders issued by Commandant General Cos, forbidding foreigners to leave the city. He further stated that three thousand troops had reached Saltillo on their way to Texas. And he promised to be with the chief in a few days' time.

Then Jim rode on to San Felipe. Event piled on event. President Santa Anna dissolved the legislatures of Cohuila and Texas and demanded that all provinces reduce their militia to one man for each five hundred inhabitants. Not only did this arouse the anger of the Texans, but many of the former members of the Mexican governing party joined with them in shouting for war against Santa Anna.

Impetuous William Barrett Travis, a lawyer who aspired to leadership of the War party, led a band of Americans to Anáhuac, captured the customs house with its store of arms and ammunition and forced Captain Antonio Tenorio and forty-four Mexican troops to surrender. He afterward released them upon their promise never to take up arms against Texas again.

Bowie was visiting Sam Houston when he heard this news. Both men groaned. "Travis will get us into war now, I'm afraid," Houston said.

Bowie nodded. These two intelligent men had been cautioning their countrymen to avoid action which would plunge them into revolution for which they were ill prepared, since Texas was divided by the war and peace factions and was without leadership.

At this critical time Austin, who had been imprisoned

in Mexico City for many months, was released and returned to Texas. Though broken in health, he was still dedicated to the cause of his colonists.

Early in September of 1835 he arrived at Velasco. Texas turned out to give him a wholehearted welcome. At a banquet held in his honor he said, "Texas needs peace and local government. Its inhabitants are farmers. They need a calm and quiet life. But how can anyone now remain indifferent when our right, our all, appear to be in jeopardy?"

Austin said he could see no choice except for drastic measures, and advocated that a general consultation be held as soon as possible. Four days later this meeting was held.

Austin had sent a message to Ugartecha deploring the impetuous action of Travis at Anáhuac. The Mexican commander at San Antonio demanded the arrest of Travis and his followers. This, of course, the Texans would not tolerate, but before the election could be held, Texas was plunged into war with Mexico.

Now Jim Bowie did not have time to think about his own tragedy. During September new crises arose. General Cos, Santa Anna's brother-in-law, landed on the southern coast of Copano with five hundred troops and immediately began a march by way of Goliad toward San Antonio. From San Felipe came notices warning "every man of Texas who cherishes liberty to prepare for war. All hope of peaceful settlement is gone."

Santa Anna made no secret of his aims to overrun Texas. In one of his frenzies he shouted, "If the Americans do not beware I shall march through their own country and plant the Mexican flag in Washington."

At another time he declared his intention of disarming

the people and driving out every American who had entered Texas since 1830, as well as punishing those who had not obeyed the regulations of the president.

Jim was riding between Nacogdoches and San Felipe when the first real clash of the Texas struggle took place at DeWitt's settlement of Gonzales. In 1831 the colonists of this place had been given a brass cannon as defense against the Indians. As their first effort to disarm the Americans, the Mexicans sent Captain Castenada from Bexar with two hundred men, demanding the cannon.

The Texans sent back the answer, "Come and take it."

The news spread quickly and volunteers gathered, armed with squirrel guns, rifles and the inevitable Bowie knife.

Just before the battle DeWitt's daughter made a flag from a sheet and painted upon it a black cannon surrounded by the words, "COME AND TAKE IT," which was placed on the cannon.

The brass cannon was turned on those who had come to take it, and within a short time the Mexican force was routed with serious losses. Not a man of the Texas band was scratched.

The victorious Texans gave a wild "yipee" as they wheeled the cannon back to the settlement, their banner proudly flying above their heads. This Battle of Gonzales, fought October 2, 1835, was the first blow for independence.

Bowie's heart beat fast when he heard the news at San Felipe. He had not wanted his countrymen to become involved in war, but ever since his secret visit to Matamoros he knew that a clash was inevitable. The mounting tension, added to his grief, had him keyed up to the bursting point. It was a relief to have the thing settled—to know where he stood. Of course he would fight with his countrymen!

Austin sent messengers to the various settlements to carry the news of the "Come and Take It" victory. Colonists rode toward Gonzales from all directions.

Meantime fifty volunteers, sparked by Bowie's friend Old Ben Milam, aged forty-four, stormed the Mexican fort of Goliad and seized about ten thousand dollars' worth of military supplies—material sorely needed by the Texans.

Bowie rode with all haste toward Gonzales to join the Texans. He overtook the army where it was encamped on the banks of the Guadalupe River awaiting reinforcements. Stephen Austin and Sam Houston were both there.

Austin had already been elected commander in chief of the Volunteer Army of Texas—the "People's Army." Also the vote had been cast to march on Bexar and attack.

Houston spoke against such impetuous action. "We aren't ready," he said. "Our men are untrained, undisciplined. Cos's army is trained, experienced, strong and well armed."

"Also well entrenched behind strong walls at Bexar," Jim added.

But those who advised caution were shouted down.

Jim went to Austin and offered his services.

"We need men of your caliber, Bowie," Austin said. "I appoint you volunteer aide, carrying the honorary rank of colonel."

Jim wished that Sam Houston had been chosen leader, for Austin was no warrior and was ill, besides. But Houston was new in Texas and had expressed himself against hasty action. Such a point of view was unpopular with the Texans who were sure they could easily whip the Mexican army and wanted to get on with the job.

On October 12th the People's Army started the march on San Antonio de Bexar. Bowie had to suppress a smile as he saw them set out. They were as ragtag an army as had ever marched to battle. Some of them were in buckskin, like himself; some in linsey-woolsey. Some wore wool hats, others coonskin caps or handkerchiefs around their heads. They were armed with old-fashioned muskets, horse pistols, double-barreled fowling pieces, broadswords—any sort of weapon they could lay hands on. But nearly every man carried a Bowie knife at his belt. Some were mounted; many walked. But there was no lack of fighting spirit.

The straggling army marched to San Francisco de la Espada, one of the abandoned early Spanish missions. There they rested while Bowie was sent in command of two companies to choose a suitable spot to establish a camp as close as possible to Bexar.

With ninety-two horsemen, Bowie set out over country he knew well. His men had confidence in him, for they knew of his victory on the San Saba River. They rode first to the San Juan Capistrano Mission. But Jim could see no favorable military positions here, so he continued on.

Two miles south of Bexar he selected a bend in the San Antonio River, about five hundred yards from the towered Concepción Mission.

Well pleased with the natural advantages of the site, Bowie placed guards in the cupola of the mission house which overlooked the whole country.

At dawn next day, such a heavy mist lay over the land

that Henry Karnes, who had just been relieved of duty in one of the towers, had to pick his way back to camp. Although he could detect no movement in the mesquite, the sound of rifle fire drew him up short. It seemed to come from the tower. A shot cracked from the plains in front of the river. Then, through the mist, Karnes detected shadowy forms and felt something slap his side.

He dashed toward camp yelling, "They're here, boys! And the danged rascals've shot out the bottom of my powder horn!"

At the first shot the Texans fired into the mist, although they could not sight their targets.

Bowie ran along the river bottom shouting, "Wait until you can see what you're shooting at and make every shot count. Keep your heads down. We haven't a man to lose."

He set them to clearing away the bushes and vines under the hill and along the edge of the bluff. At the steepest places he had steps dug in the side of the bluff so that they could ascend to fire, then drop below the bank to reload.

The rising sun dispelled the mist and revealed the advancing Mexican infantry, supported by five companies of cavalry—about four hundred Mexican soldiers, to Bowie's ninety-two men.

The harsh crack of rifle fire opened the battle about eight o'clock that chilly morning. At once the firing became general. From the Mexican side it presented a steady sheet of flame. The Texans fired with deadly accuracy, then ducked below the bank to reload.

A Texas sharpshooter picked off the mule driver in charge of the caisson carrying the ammunition. The team raced through the Mexican lines creating great confusion.

The battle had scarcely begun when the enemy brought up a big brass cannon which they trained on the American line.

"Pick off the cannon, men!" Bowie shouted.

One by one the artillerymen manning the cannon were killed, only to be replaced by others. Another charge from the four-pounder blasted through the timber. At the same time the cavalry charged, but so deadly was the Texans' aim that they were repelled.

Three times foot soldiers attempted to charge across the plains, but each time they were forced to fall back, leaving the prairie littered with bodies.

Finally Jim roared, "Let's take the cannon, boys! Follow me! The cannon and victory."

He dashed from the thicket, pistol in hand, a band of his men right at his heels, their guns spitting fire. The Mexicans ran. With a yell the Bowie men seized the cannon and turned it on the fleeing enemy. Someone grabbed the brand from the hand of a dead Mexican and applied it to the vent.

With triumphant shouts the other Americans poured over the edge of the bluff. Seeing them, the Mexicans broke and ran toward Bexar. The entire Battle of Concepción had lasted only half an hour, but it was a smashing victory which greatly cheered the Americans and did much to enhance Jim Bowie's glory.

There were sixteen bodies around the captured cannon. One hundred more Mexican soldiers lost their lives, against only one casualty for the Texans.

Chapter Nineteen

FALSE VICTORY

Austin rode to join the main troops at Concepción. James Bowie and Captains Fannin and Briscoe rode out to meet him. If they expected any praise for their smashing victory they were disappointed.

"You should have followed them," Austin said peevishly. "With the enemy so demoralized, you could have smashed into San Antonio."

Bowie stared at him in surprise. "You seem to have forgotten, suh, that you gave me written orders not to do so."

Austin ignored him. "With our combined forces we should push on without delay. Drive them from Bexar."

"Such a course would be foolhardy," Bowie said. "I do not wish to dispute your authority as commander in chief, suh. But as a long-time resident of Bexar I know the fortifications of the city. They have been greatly altered during the two years you were a prisoner in Mexico. Our men are brave fighters, but it would be folly to send a small force against such strongly entrenched enemies."

Austin's thin lips tightened. "What do you think about it, Fannin?"

"I agree with Bowie," the captain said.

While he was speaking Briscoe nodded.

"Nonsense! Sheer nonsense!" Austin put heel to his horse. His subordinates said nothing, but Bowie knew what was in their minds. Austin had been dedicated to the interests of his colonists, but he was a misfit as a military leader and had as little heart as ability for his present role.

Jim was dumfounded the following morning when Austin announced his intention of skirting around Bexar and entrenching the main army at the Old Mill, about a mile north of the Alamo—on the opposite side of San Antonio from Concepción.

"I consider it a more strategic point," he said. "Bowie, you and your command will remain here and daily demonstrate before the enemy position. I have reason to think that many Mexicans will desert to our side with a little show of force."

Jim clamped his mouth shut tight so that he would not voice further criticism of his commander in chief. He realized that Austin was not used to being contradicted and that although he did not relish his present position, he took it very seriously. Also, Jim knew that Austin greatly resented his friendship with Sam Houston, who was rapidly growing more powerful.

Every day Bowie went through the ridiculous farce of making a "show of force" before the enemy with his ninety men. And nearly every day he dispatched a mes sage to Austin expressing his opinion that the force. should be united.

Nothing happened. His men became bored. One or two at a time they drifted away.

"It's time for a showdown," Jim told Fannin. "I'm sending in my resignation to Austin."

"You can't do that," Fannin said. "The men have confidence in you."

"I can and have done so," Bowie said. He handed Fannin the letter he had just finished writing. After tender ing his resignation, Jim had written:

> I deem it of the utmost importance for you to effect a union of the army as soon as practicable. Great dissatisfaction now exists in this division, and unless counteracted by the measure suggested, I seriously apprehend the dissolution of it.

Before this letter reached Austin, however, Jim received instructions from him to march his detachment and join with the main force at the Old Mill.

As soon as the Bowie-Fannin division reached them, Austin called a council of war and again brought up his demand for an immediate assault on Bexar. Again his officers voted him down. Finally they prevailed upon him to leave a small company at the mill and take the main force to the strategic location at Concepción to await reinforcements and the arrival of an eighteen-pound cannon reported to be on the way.

Then, while the colonists in San Felipe argued endlessly about drafting plans for a provisional government, the restless volunteers lay around Concepción grumbling.

"How can Austin talk of taking Bexar," one lanky fellow complained to Bowie. "We haven't even any ammunition for the one dinky four-pounder we took from the Mexicans."

Jim chuckled. "We can fix that. And liven things up a bit for you fellows, too. Follow me!"

A handful of curious volunteers mounted their horses and rode behind Bowie, who whooped and fired his pistol close to the enemy line.

He got the desired result. The Mexicans, evidently

believing an attack had started, fired their cannon, while Jim led his daring companions out of danger. Later they went out and gathered up the cannon balls. Every day they eased their boredom by this sport until the Mexicans grew wise to their strategy and ceased firing. However, the volunteers had gained something to feed their four-pounder when the time came to use it against its former owners.

Once more boredom settled over the little army of less than six hundred. At this time, however, new hope was injected into the ranks by the arrival of two companies of New Orleans Grays, dapper in new uniforms, with cocky flat caps and gleaming side arms. Outfitted at their own expense they had come to join the Texas fight for independence.

As they displayed their superiority over the ragtag volunteer army, its ranks continued to diminish. Yet two other companies joined: one from Mississippi and another from eastern Texas. Lanky weatherbeaten Ben Milam came riding in, saying if there was any excitement brewing he hankered to be in the middle of it.

Jim grinned at his old friend. "There's not much excitement right now," he said. "But it may start any time."

On November 18th Austin appeared in the doorway of the mission to make an announcement.

"I have a communication from San Felipe," he said. "Plans for a provisional government were drawn up on the 12th. Henry Smith was elected governor; Sam Houston, commander in chief of the army. I have been chosen to serve as commissioner to the United States. General Burleson replaces me in command here until Houston arrives. I am ready at all times to serve Texas in any station where it is considered I can be useful."

Then his head snapped up and his eyes looked coldly over the shocked volunteers as though forbidding them to show pity.

After being dismissed, his men gathered in small groups to discuss this new shift.

Bowie turned to Ben Milam. "There have been times when I wanted to wring Austin's neck. He's no military man. But now I admire him. He took his demotion like a man. He should be president of the provisional government. There wouldn't be any Texas if it weren't for him! What has Smith ever done?"

Jim walked away puzzling over the inconsistencies of political fortunes. He believed, though, that Sam Houston was the right man to be commander in chief.

Volunteers continued to straggle into camp from the States. Some recruits brought in two small artillery pieces to add to the four-pounder Bowie had captured at the Battle of Concepción. Bowie established contact with some of Urselita's kin in the city who informed him that Cos was expecting Ugartecha with money to pay the eight hundred Mexican soldiers.

Bowie planned to head off the Ugartecha force. He sent his old friend Deaf Smith out to scout.

On the morning of the 26th Deaf Smith galloped into camp on a lather-flecked horse. "It's them," he cried. "The money train. Ugartecha with a strong force."

"Bowie!" Burleson shouted. "Take as many men as you need and go out and intercept the train. I'll follow up with the infantry."

Bowie strode through the camp, choosing forty men. As they went over the old Presidio Road the men shouted to each other that they were going to sink their arms to the elbows in Mexican money.

Four miles beyond they spied the Mexican column. Bowie ordered his men to dismount, tie their horses in clumps of mesquite and take cover in a near-by arroyo.

When the Mexicans came within gunshot Bowie gave the signal to fire. Several dragoons were brought down. The Mexicans promptly took refuge behind the bank of a dry creek bed. Both sides banged away without doing any harm. Then the firing ceased. During this interval Bowie saw Burleson leading the infantry across the open plain.

"Go back! You fools!" he shouted.

Burleson had led his division directly between the two lines. The Mexicans opened fire. The Texas infantry scattered over the prairie.

"Let's get 'em, boys!" Jim shouted.

He scrambled from the ravine, followed by his forty men. They were joined by about fifty of the infantrymen who had by this time collected their wits. Without the loss of a single man, they routed the Mexicans from their creek bed, leaving about thirty dead.

The whooping Texans gleefully gathered the sixty horses and burros with their precious packs.

"Mexican money!" some of the volunteers cried. "Let's divide the loot."

Chuckling, Jim yanked out his knife and slit open one of the sacks. Freshly cut grass slipped out upon the ground. The men stared openmouthed while Jim slit open another sack. More grass! He repeated the performance three more times. Then it dawned on everyone that this was not Ugartecha with the pay roll from Laredo, but merely a foraging party carrying grass to Bexar to feed Cos's livestock.

The Texans whooped with laughter, shouting, slapping each other on the shoulders, rolling on the ground. Jim forced himself to laugh with them, but he felt that this attack had made him ridiculous. The men wouldn't forget it for a long time. Nor did they. Jokes about the "Grass Fight" relieved the tedium around camp until Jim Bowie was heartily sick of it.

On December 3rd, Burleson called for a general council of war to decide whether to attack Bexar or retire to winter quarters at Goliad or Gonzales. The decision was made to go into winter quarters. Bowie spoke up in meeting for this plan, feeling sure that Sam Houston, their commander in chief, was raising reinforcements, and they should await word from him.

Next day, while baggage was being packed for the evacuation, a Mexican deserter rode into camp, reporting that the defenses at Bexar were weak and that the Americans could easily take the place.

Burleson put no stock in the report but fiery Ben Milam shouted, "Now's the time! Who'll go with Old Ben Milam into San Antonio!"

Two hundred men stepped out to follow. General Burleson gave grudging permission for Milam to take whatever men wished to volunteer and make the attack. He would hold the remainder in readiness for whatever support might be needed.

Milam set out with three hundred volunteers armed with crowbars as well as firearms. Bowie was sorry now that he had spoken so strongly for waiting. He was like an old war horse champing at the bit to get into battle. But he hesitated to go back on his own statement.

However, he directed a steady firing on the Alamo to divert the attention of the Mexicans while Milam led his brave men in a house-to-house attack toward Military Plaza where Cos had his main defenses.

For four long days Bowie kept up his blasting while listening to gunshots and shouts within the city.

Then on the morning of December 9th the Mexicans raised the white flag. Bexar was won, but Ben Milam had paid for it with his life.

Bowie rode with Burleson to the Alamo where Cos has retired to accept the surrender and sign the papers stating that he agreed to withdraw all Mexican military beyond the Rio Grande and to swear that he would never again oppose the re-establishment of the Constitution of 1824 in Texas.

The triumph of the Texans knew no bounds. They had cleared the province of all Mexican soldiers. Now, they believed, they could go home and enjoy Christmas with their families, plant their crops in the spring and settle down to normal living.

Bowie went into Bexar to visit the Navarros. "I'm afraid this is only the beginning," he told his uncle. "Santa Anna won't take this defeat. We should dig in and really prepare for war."

"That Santa Anna is the Devil incarnate," Navarro said. "I'm afraid there will be more and bloodier war than any we've yet seen."

"Tomorrow," Jim went on, "I'm going to ride to San Felipe to talk with Sam Houston. I want a commission to raise a regiment of troops and train them myself."

But on the next day, Bowie found himself confronted

with a new emergency. Many of the Texans thought that when Cos was driven from Bexar the war was over and had gone home. Yet there was a scheme afoot which appealed to the imaginations of most of the adventurers who had come to fight for Texas independence and who felt they were being cheated of the excitement they had expected to find.

Chapter Twenty

GATHERING STORM CLOUDS

James Bowie had mistrusted Dr. Grant when he first joined the Army of the People. The Mexicans had taken over his country estate in Coahuila, so it was natural that he should seek vengeance. He had been with the command only a few days when he began urging an attack upon Matamoros—to cut the Mexicans off at their source of supply.

Bowie shrugged the plan off as so much visionary talk. If the Texans had sufficient force they could carry it out, but weak and divided as they were, it was too impracticable. Yet after the defeat of Cos, Jim was alarmed to see that many of the volunteers were paying attention to the doctor. Even Fannin had joined his ranks and since Fannin was a West Point man, the recruits from the States threw in their lot with him.

One morning Bowie found a proclamation stuck to the wall of one of the buildings at Goliad stating that volunteers with Grant and Fannin would be paid "out of the first spoils taken from the enemy." It was boldly signed by Colonel J. W. Fannin, "acting commander in chief."

Despite Jim's protests that they were acting without authority from the real commander in chief, the cream of the army rode off. One of the arrogant young adventurers from Louisiana threw over his shoulder, "Go find another grass fight, Jim Bowie," and laughter swept through the ranks. Jim had led two victorious charges against overwhelming numbers, yet it was this one humiliating mistake that his comrades remembered.

He turned and called for his servant Ham to bring his horse. He had no definite plan of action; he merely wanted to get away from this nearly deserted post where only thirty men remained.

On the road leading from town he saw a rider coming from the east. He gave a shout of joy—"Sam Houston! Never have my eyes seen a more welcome sight."

"Where are they?" Houston demanded.

"Who do you mean?"

"That rascal Grant and those he's trying to lead to attack Matamoros solely for the purpose of getting back his own property."

"They rode away this morning."

"Then I must hurry and overtake them."

"You'll need a fresh horse," Bowie pointed out. "And some food and rest yourself."

"I'll eat. And beg a fresh mount," Houston agreed. "Then I must be on my way."

"Everything is in a mess," Houston said as they rode into Goliad. "At a time when we should stand united, everyone is pulling in different directions. Governor Smith has no hold over the people. They should have elected Austin. The settlers respected and obeyed him."

"Then tossed him out when they needed him most." There was bitterness in Jim's tone. "I had hoped for a commission from you to recruit and train a force."

"No one deserves it more," Houston said. "You're the best fighting man we have, Jim Bowie. Oh, I know how you feel about it! Buck Travis was made a colonel because he captured a herd of wild horses."

"He was Austin's favorite," Jim said quietly.

"Fannin was promoted because of your brilliant work at Concepción when he was your aide. Yet you still have a kind word for Austin. You're a big man, Jim. You see how it is. Those men were settlers, whereas you married a highborn Mexican girl. So a cloud of suspicion still clings to you."

"I'm heart and soul for Texas in her fight for independence from Santa Anna," Jim said. "Tell me what to do, Sam."

"I wish that there were more like you," Houston said. "I had a desperate letter from Colonel Neill at the Alamo, saying that Santa Anna has four thousand men at Laredo. Neill has only one hundred men and you have thirty here. May God save Texas! Oh, Bowie, what am I to do? I should be galloping toward the runaway army and persuading it to come back. Did any commander in chief ever have his army stolen from under his nose?"

"I doubt it," Jim responded.

"Neill pleads for help. I should be in San Felipe trying to help hold the government together and to muster troops. I could do it, Jim, if I just had more time!"

"Tell me how I can best serve you," Jim repeated.

"Ride to the Alamo. If Santa Anna is really in Laredo we'll need all our forces to stop him along the way. Evacuate the troops from the Alamo, remove the cannon and blow up the place. But use your own judgment. I trust you, Jim."

The men rode off in different directions. Bowie ordered his thirty men to follow him to Bexar.

He rode straight to the Alamo, to confer with Colonel Neill, an impatient man.

"You say you're bringing only thirty men?" he asked pettishly.

"That's every man there was at Goliad." Jim's tone was calm.

"I tell you the Mexicans are already on the march. What can we do with a mere handful of men?"

"Let me study the situation here. I want to look over the Alamo."

"Do so," Neill snapped. "You will see that a thousand men could not hold the place."

Jim had, of course, seen the ancient mission many times, but he had never before looked at it as a possible military fortification. The vast extent of the outer wall was its worst weakness. Neill was right. At least a thousand men would be required to defend it.

The Alamo was in the same condition that General Cos had left it at his surrender the previous December. The rear wall of the chapel—the building known today as the Alamo—had crumbled. Only at the front was any of the flat roof left. Jim decided that this would serve as a platform for a cannon. The inside of the chapel was piled high with debris, yet its thick walls might lend protection for a last-ditch stand.

As there were no loopholes the riflemen would have to stand on earthen platforms to shoot over the top, with their heads, shoulders, and arms exposed.

Mounds would have to be erected for the emplacement of the cannon. A feeling of hopelessness seized Jim when he saw there were no structural features to aid in defense.

With sufficient men willing to work, the place eventually might be made into an adequate fortification. But like Houston, Jim felt the desperate need for time—more time.

Before conferring again with Colonel Neill he rode into Bexar. A lump came into his throat when he passed the Veramendi *palacio*. The huge carved cedar door hung open, half torn from its hinges. The white adobe walls were pock-marked with rifle bullets and there was a great wound in the side wall where the Texans had crashed through with their crowbars.

He went to the Navarro home and Don José seized his arm with a cry of welcome as he drew him inside the house.

"I have a grave decision to make," Bowie told him. "I have instructions from Sam Houston to clear the Alamo and blow it up. But he told me to act at my discretion. What do you think? Do you believe that Santa Anna has a force already on Texas soil?"

"I know he has," Navarro answered.

"What do you and others in Bexar think of the matter?"

"Need you ask?" Don José said reprovingly. "Within a few days I leave for San Felipe as a delegate to the convention summoned to meet March 1st to declare independence, elect a president and adopt a constitution. As you know, your old friend Juan Seguin is a captain with Neill. His nephew Blaz Herraera is at this moment doing valuable duty as a scout."

"Will the common people help us fight Santa Anna?" Jim asked.

Navarro shook his head and smiled ruefully. "They have a horrible fear of that devil. They have heard of his massacre of the people of Zacatecas, when he stood hundreds against a wall and slaughtered them in cold blood. If Santa Anna comes, the people of Bexar will run, not fight—and who can blame them?"

Bowie stood up. His jaw was set and his eyes blazed. "Thank you, Don José," he said. "You have helped me make up my mind."

"And what is your decision, nephew?"

"To hold the Alamo at all costs. It is the keystone of Texas—the only bulwark to hold Santa Anna from storming through the province, burning and slaughtering, as he did in Zacatecas."

Jim rode back to the Alamo and told Colonel Neill his plan.

"Hold the Alamo with so few men?" Neill scoffed. "Are you crazy, man?"

Jim shook his head. "I was never more sane in my life. I *know* this is what we must do. Every hour that we can delay Santa Anna gives Houston that much more time to muster an army to reinforce us."

Bowie spoke with such conviction that Neill finally agreed.

Jim thereupon wrote to Governor Henry Smith that the salvation of Texas depended on keeping Bexar out of enemy hands. And that both he and Colonel Neill would "rather die in these ditches than give up to the enemy." He asked for relief, stating that they had only one hundred and twenty men against the enemy's thousands.

A few days after Bowie dispatched this letter, Buck Travis rode into Bexar at the head of thirty men. Neill greeted him with such enthusiasm that Bowie was surprised, although he had suspected that the colonel had definitely cooled off in his desire to "die in these ditches."

Next day Neill announced that he had received news

that a member of his family was gravely ill and he must leave immediately. As he rode off he threw over his shoulder, "I leave you in charge, Travis."

Bowie flushed angrily. "He has no right to turn the command over to you," he said hoarsely. "Sam Houston considers that I am in charge."

"Neill and I are regular army," Travis said, arrogantly.

"And I am only a volunteer, eh?" Jim roared. "Well, if you are so set on military procedure, I outrank you a long way by right of seniority. I remind you that I am forty-one and you can't be more than twenty-eight. Until our commander in chief sends word that I am to be relieved, I remain in command here."

Still fuming, Bowie called for his horse and rode into Bexar. He strode into one of the *cantinas* where he saw a buckskin-clad fellow sprawled at one of the tables. The eyes of the two men met. Although Jim had never seen this weatherbeaten face before, there was something about that humorous, sly expression and the shrewd look in the gray eyes that attracted him.

"I'll bet you be Jim Bowie," the stranger said.

"That's right. And you?"

"Davy Crockett from Tennessee. I heard about the ruckus here in Texas, so I took old Betsey"—he put his hand affectionately on the barrel of his long rifle—"and gathered up a band of twelve scrappers and trekked out here to get in on the fun."

"I can assure you that you're more than welcome," Jim said, laughing.

"Let me see that knife of yourn I've heard so much about."

Jim laid his knife on the table.

Crockett picked it up and examined it, turning it over

and over. "Tarnation!" he exclaimed. "The very sight of this is enough to give a man a squeamish stomach—'specially afore breakfast!"

Crockett handed the weapon back and drew his own knife from its sheath. "Mine was made in Bristol, England. Pretty good copy, I'd say. Every man in my company's got one like it."

"Good!" Jim said. "I'm mighty glad you've come to help us. I've a feeling that before long you and your men will find all the excitement you want."

Jim Bowie was not the only one disturbed by Neill's appointment of Travis to take command of the defense of the Alamo. The volunteers took up the quarrel in earnest, and the matter created such a hubbub that Travis was forced to put it to a vote. Jim Bowie won by an overwhelming margin.

Travis took his defeat with such bad grace that the force which should have been readying the Alamo for battle continued to spend valuable time quarreling.

Finally Jim went to Travis. "This won't do," he said. "Unity between us is more important than personal ambition. I suggest that you take charge of the regular army, while I command the volunteers. Then I believe our men will pull together."

So the matter was finally settled agreeably and the forces at last began to work at the tremendous task of fortifying the Alamo.

Chapter Twenty-one

BLAZE OF GLORY

Bowie and Travis built barricades of earth tamped between cowhides, opening into the various rooms which would serve as barracks. Platforms of earth lined the inner walls to provide places for the riflemen to stand. Although a ditch flowed through the grounds, there was danger that the Mexicans would cut off the water supply, and so a well was dug.

Jim worked feverishly to set the fourteen cannon, left behind by Cos after his surrender, in the best position for defense. All ammunition was stored in the sacristy of the chapel. Over the rampart waved the Mexican flag of 1824, showing that the Texans would still abide by the constitution of that year.

On the morning of February 23rd, 1836, the bell in the tower of the San Fernando Church, where a sentinel had been posted, clanged violently.

Soon a messenger galloped from Bexar with the news that the Mexican troops were on the heights of Alazan. Deaf Smith and Dr. John Sutherland were sent out to scout. In a short time they came back shouting that the Mexican army was in sight.

Then the exodus from Bexar began. Frightened householders piled personal belongings on clumsy two-wheeled carts and joined the long lines clogging the roads leading to the country. Volunteers of the People's Army hurried to the Alamo. Even one woman joined them there, the wife of Almaron Dickerson, with her infant daughter.

Jim Bowie was standing on a cedar platform supervising the mounting of a large cannon above the gate. The pulley screeched; the cannon commenced to swing dangerously.

"Look out!" someone shouted from below.

Bowie stepped back—into nothingness. His arms flailed, searching for something to grasp. His body struck the ground. There was a blinding flash, then blackness.

The worried face of Dr. Edward Mitchason bent over Jim, while skilled fingers probed gently, yet sent stabs of pain through his chest. Bowie choked, coughed and glanced up at the doctor in alarm when he saw a blot of red stain the ground.

"I've broken something, Doc," he said.

"I'm afraid that a rib has penetrated the lung," Mitchason said with deep concern.

Bowie struggled to his feet. "I can't be bothered with a little thing like that now," he gasped.

"I've taped your chest," the doctor said. "It's all I can do. Any strenuous action, however, will only worsen your condition—prolong your recovery."

Jim laughed as he swayed to his feet. "Santa Anna won't wait for my recovery. I'll keep going as long as I can."

And keep going he did, for a time, although every movement was agony.

Santa Anna sent a message demanding unconditional surrender. The answer was a cannon shot directed at an enemy group gathered at the main plaza. This shot opened that epic struggle on February 23, 1836. All day long as cannon boomed and rifles cracked, Bowie managed to stay on his feet directing operations. But by night he sank to his cot, coughing and shaking with chills.

Next morning he tried to rise, but the world whirled crazily. Worse than the terrible pain was the spiritual agony because at this critical hour he was unable to take part in the fighting. It had been his decision to take this stand and hold the Alamo at all costs. Therefore he should be directing its defense.

He sent his servant Ham to summon Travis. "I won't be much use to you now," he gasped. "I pass my command on to you."

Travis leaned over and grasped his hand. "You'll be better in a day or so," he said. "By then, perhaps we'll have reinforcements. I'd like to have you read this letter which I'm sending out by courier after dark tonight."

Jim read:

Commandancy of the Alamo, Bexar
Feb'y 24, 1836

To the People of Texas and all Americans in the World:

FELLOW CITIZENS AND COMPATRIOTS: I am besieged by a thousand or more Mexicans under Santa Anna. I have sustained continual bombardment for 24 hours and have not lost a man. The enemy has demanded surrender at discretion; otherwise the garrison are to be put to the sword, if the fort is taken. I have answered the demand with a cannon shot, and our flag still flies proudly from the walls. I shall never surrender or retreat. Then, I call on you in the name of Liberty, of Patriotism, and everything dear to the American character, to come to our aid with all dispatch. The enemy is receiving reinforcements daily and will no doubt increase to three or four thousand in four or five days. If this call is neglected, I am determined to sustain myself as long as possible and die like a soldier who never forgets what is due to his own honor and that of his country. Victory or Death!

WILLIAM BARRETT TRAVIS,
Lt. Col. Comdt.

"Noble words," Bowie gasped. "Words that will go down in history."

"I feel sure," Travis said, "that if reinforcements come in time, we can hold the Alamo indefinitely, even with only fourteen pieces of artillery. But the scarcity of ball and powder worries me."

"When Fannin sees this letter," Bowie said, "he will come at once to our aid."

Travis sent frantic messages to Fannin, who had most of Texas' military strength under his control at Goliad. One courier came back with the discouraging word that Fannin had set out toward the Alamo, but because one supply train had broken down he had turned back.

The lookouts stared in vain toward the east, hoping to see a cloud of dust which would mean Fannin's army was coming. Day after day dragged by, bringing only disappointment.

At night Davy Crockett played his fiddle and pranced about, clowning to try to cheer "the boys."

The fighting went on day and night. The deadly aim of the Texas sharpshooters was taking heavy toll of Santa Anna's forces, but he had replacements to fill the gaps, for he had emptied the Mexican prisons and had taken every available man.

The doctor tried to keep Bowie in a small room above the chapel for comparative quiet from the everlasting booming, but Jim asked Ham and Davy Crockett to carry his cot down into the chapel where he could encourage the weary men as they passed back and forth to the sacristy for ammunition.

On the first of March the Alamo defenders were cheered when thirty-two men from Gonzales slipped into the fortress.

Bowie heard Travis tell them, "You've given our hearts a lift, boys. We thought the world had forgotten us. We'll hold out. Santa Anna has fired over two hundred cannon balls into the Alamo, but we haven't lost a man. We fire the balls right back at them. What's Sam Houston doing? Why doesn't he send us some help?"

Jim was shocked when he heard one of the newcomers say, "Sam Houston's off dickering with the Cherokee to keep them from attacking the settlements. Santa Anna's been egging them on to do that very thing. The council kicked both Smith and Houston out. Right now Texas has no government at all—and no commander in chief. All the council does is squabble."

Jim groaned and turned his face away. He had struggled so hard to hold this Texas keystone in order to give Sam Houston time. Now those fools in San Felipe were spoiling everything by their everlasting bickering.

Bowie was determined to get well quickly. But for once he had met something he could not conquer. Every breath he drew was like a knife gashing the inside of his chest. Most of the time he either burned with fever or shook with chills. There were times of wild delirium during which he was soothed by the gentle hands of Mrs. Dickerson as she bathed his face.

Awaking from a restless sleep, he found that an ominous silence had fallen.

Davy Crockett loomed in the doorway. "How ye doing, Jim? Me and Betsey's been too busy pickin' off Mexicans to pay you much attention."

"I wish I could have been with you," Bowie said in a faint voice. "I'm not gaining very fast, Davy. What's happening out there? Why is it so quiet?"

"Don't rightly know. Maybe the Mexicans are tired."

Jim shook his head. Perhaps this was the lull before the real storm, he thought. Now and then he heard voices, and the tramping of feet.

"I want to be out where I can see what's going on," he said.

Crockett yelled for three of his comrades to help carry Jim's cot to where the troops had assembled. The men were unshaven, dirty, haggard—obviously bone weary, starved for sleep.

"What's the date?" Bowie asked Crockett.

"March 3rd." Crockett replied.

"Has the battle been going on for ten days?" Jim was incredulous.

Crockett nodded. "Day and night. Ain't one of us has had a bit of sleep except what we could grab between rifle shots."

"How can human beings endure it?" Bowie wondered aloud.

"We can bear it all right," Davy said. "The rations get kind of tiresome, though, nothing but beef and corn. But I reckon we're lucky to have that—and plenty of water. The Mexicans tried to dam up the ditch, but the well gives us all we need for drinkin'. Ain't got time to wash nohow."

Travis' voice rang out. "Gather around, men, I want to speak to you."

Bowie was shocked at the change in the leader. His face was haggard; his mouth bracketed by lines of fatigue.

"My brave companions," Travis said in a voice husky with emotion, "I am compelled to tell you that within a few days—perhaps hours—we must all be in eternity. We cannot avoid it. It is our certain doom.

"We are surrounded by an enemy that could almost eat us for breakfast, from whose arms our lives are, for the present, protected by these stone walls. We have no hope of help, for no force could get through the strong ranks of these Mexicans. We dare not surrender, for we know what fate we would meet at the hands of our enemies. If we attempt to escape we would all be slain in less than ten minutes. Nothing remains but to stay within this fort and fight to the last moment. Sooner or later we must all be killed, for I am sure that Santa Anna will storm the fort and take it, at whatever it may cost in the lives of his own men.

"Then we must die! Our business is not to make a fruitless effort to save our lives, but to choose the manner of our death by which we may best serve our country. The Mexican army is strong enough to march through the land and exterminate its inhabitants. Our countrymen are not able to oppose them in open field. My choice, then, is to remain in this fort, to resist every assault and to sell our lives as dearly as possible."

"Hurray!" Bowie's voice was weak, although he put all

his strength into this cheer. Instantly it was taken up by the men until the walls echoed.

Travis went on: "Then let us band together as brothers and vow to die together. Let us resolve to withstand our enemies to the last, and at each advance to kill as many of them as possible. Let us kill them as they scale our walls! Kill them as they leap within! Kill them as they raise their weapons and as they use them! And continue to kill them as long as one of us shall remain alive!

"By this policy I trust that we shall so weaken our enemies that our countrymen at home can meet them on fair terms, cut them up, expel them from our country and thus establish their own independence.

"But I leave every man to his own choice. Should any man prefer to surrender or to attempt to escape, he is at liberty to do so.

"My choice is to stay here and die for my country, fighting as long as breath remains in my body. This I will do, even if you leave me alone."

A great wave of emotion swept through Bowie as Travis concluded his speech. He looked over the grave faces of the men as they stood in line. It was apparent that those inspired words had put new energy into them.

Travis drew a line with his sword on the ground before the volunteers. "I now want every man who is determined to stay here and die with me to come across this line. Who will be first?"

Bowie's spirits rose when he saw young Tapley Holland leap across the line shouting, "I am ready to die for my country!"

In a moment all save Bowie and William Rose were standing on Travis' side of the line.

Jim mustered all his strength and called, "Hey, Davy, I want to be with you. Lift me across the line."

Four pairs of willing hands seized the corners of his cot and bore him across. Now everyone was on the side of Travis but William Rose, a trader who had fought well enough.

"What's the matter, man?" New strength had come to Bowie's voice. "You aren't afraid to fight with your comrades, are you?"

There was a long silence and then Rose said, "I'm willing to fight, but not to die and I won't if I can help it. I'm dark enough to pass for a Mexican and I speak their dialect. I think I have a chance to escape."

"Nonsense," Crockett's nasal twang broke out. "You'd better stay with us, old man. Escape ain't possible."

Rose stared wildly at the top of the wall. Then he ran and scrambled up and over.

"Anyone want to follow him?" Travis' curt voice broke the stunned silence.

A resounding chorus of "noes" was his reply.

"Clean your rifles, reload them and back to your posts," Travis said. "The attack may recommence at any moment."

Then after a pause, he said, "I charge the last man left alive to fire the powder magazine—blow up the Alamo."

Not a shot was fired during the entire night. Santa Anna could not have devised a more fiendish and effective method of catching the gallant defenders off guard. They had been keyed up to battle pitch for so long that under pressure they could have carried on indefinitely. But with the lull came the overpowering desire to sleep, and when they gave way they were as though drugged.

Bowie had asked to be left beside the wall with the other sick and wounded. He woke now and then with a start, wondering about the unwonted stillness.

Two hours before dawn the attack started again, but this time above the roar of gunfire came a bloodcurdling sound—the bands playing the dread *deguello*—which meant: "No quarter. Slaughter the enemy."

Jim Bowie, helpless on his cot, knew its meaning, as did every man on the walls.

Ham told him that Santa Anna had run up a blood red flag over the San Fernando Church.

"This is the end, Ham," Bowie said calmly. "Load four pistols and lay them and my knife close to my hand. Go where you can see what's going on and come and tell me."

Soon Ham reported that the Mexicans had surrounded three sides of the Alamo—that they were carrying scaling ladders but that two attempts to climb the walls had been driven back.

"The ground out there is covered with dead men," Ham said. "It's the worst slaughter you could dream of. Someone says the officers are slapping the soldiers with their swords to keep 'em coming on."

"His victory will cost Santa Anna dearer than defeat," Bowie said.

Lying helpless on his cot, Jim was aware of the unceasing pounding and cracking of artillery, of the acrid smell of powder, of dust and sweat. He knew when the enemy was driven back by the triumphant shouts of the Texans.

Although there was little strength in his body, his senses were keener than they had ever been. He felt his cot being lifted. He opened his eyes and looked up in amazement. Ham, Davy Crockett and two others were carrying his cot into a small room.

"They've broken through," Crockett panted. "They're tumbling over the north wall. Now they'll have to take the Alamo room by room."

"Don't stick me off like this," Bowie protested. "I want to fight, too."

"Take care of him, Ham," was Davy's reply as he slammed the heavy door of the little room.

It was dark and chill inside. "Drag my cot to that corner facing the door," Bowie said. "Then crouch against the wall out of sight. Hand me the pistols. I'll use them as long as I can. Then I'll use the knife."

It seemed that he lay there waiting for hours listening to the continuous booms, bangs and yells which went on all through the inner wall and the chapel. He had heard Travis order the last man left alive to blow up the powder magazine. He waited for the explosion which did not come.

Finally the noise died down. The only shouting he heard was in Mexican dialect. Were all his comrades dead then? Was he the last one left?

The door burst open and he saw savage, wild-eyed faces staring in. He raised a pistol, pulled the trigger. One man fell. He reached for another pistol, then another and another in quick succession. Weakness had fled. New energy flowed into his wasted muscles. His deadly aim claimed four enemy lives. Now he reached for the knife as he stared up into evil faces and saw the glint of bayonets over him. His knife ripped up. There was a terrible cry and a heavy body fell across him. But Jim Bowie did not know it, for with that knife blow he gave his last ounce of energy.

And so the famous knife did its work for the final time. Fittingly enough, James Bowie, whose momentous decision it was to make that epic stand at the Alamo, delivered the last blow for freedom and was the last of her defenders to die there.

Chapter Twenty-Two

THE RECKONING

And so Jim Bowie's wish to "live to the hilt during the best years of my life, then go out in a blaze of glory" was fulfilled.

Santa Anna strode through the Alamo asking his guide from Bexar to point out to him the bodies of Travis, Bowie and Crockett—the "bravest of the brave." Then he ordered his men to bring wood to make a gigantic funeral pyre outside the walls for these bodies.

The lives of Mrs. Dickerson and her child and the servants of Travis and Bowie were spared. But Santa Anna had a purpose in such mercy.

"Tell everyone you meet," he said to Mrs. Dickerson as he sent them riding eastward, "that we will deal in this manner with anyone who opposes our march through Texas."

Meanwhile the convention to organize a new government had met at San Felipe, and the bickering broke out anew. But when Travis' brave and pathetic message reached the meeting and was read aloud, a hubbub arose to adjourn and march at once to the rescue of the Alamo.

"Don't talk like fools!" Sam Houston roared. "Precious time has already been lost. The first thing we must do is organize a government so that Texas will have leadership. Then our men will flock to her defense. I will ride to the front, raising troops as I go and interpose them between the enemy and our seat of government. Then if mortal power can avail I will relieve the brave men in the Alamo."

He left the convention, clad as he had come from his meeting with the Cherokee. He mounted a fast horse and with only four men rode toward Gonzales after sending a messenger to Goliad with word for Fannin to bring his troops and meet him.

On the afternoon of March 11th, Houston was heartened to find at Gonzales a volunteer force of three hundred and seventy-four men, with two cannon, who were awaiting a leader. Still nothing was heard from Fannin.

Houston was organizing the force into companies when Deaf Smith rode in with Mrs. Dickerson, her little daughter and the two Negro servants.

In a matter of moments came the news of the fall of the Alamo. Then reports were circulated that the Mexican army was in sight. Only a man of Houston's forcefulness could have stemmed the tide of panic.

He prepared for a midnight retreat, with a rear guard to protect the refugees who would swell as the army moved east.

Houston had no way of knowing that Santa Anna was still in Bexar licking his wounds from the terrific mauling the heroes of the Alamo had given his army. Sixteen hundred of the pick of the Mexican troops had been killed, and hundreds more wounded. Before he could do further damage he must completely reorganize his forces. Bowie's decision to defend the Alamo had given Texas twelve precious days.

The tremendous sacrifices of the defenders of the Alamo were not in vain. This delay saved the American colonies in Texas from Santa Anna's threat to conquer.

The fateful news from the Alamo finally spurred the convention at San Felipe into declaring for the independence of Texas and putting into motion the machinery of government.

As Sam Houston moved eastward he gathered both refugees and little groups of men willing to fight. Finally a courier on a lathered horse caught up with him, reporting that Santa Anna had moved on to Goliad and demanded the surrender of Fannin—under "honorable terms of war." Upon receiving this, Santa Anna ordered Fannin and his army taken out onto the plains and killed.

While Houston moved to the Colorado River, Santa Anna stormed across the country, pillaging and burning the deserted farms and towns. The runaway army threatened to depose Houston as commander in chief if he did not take a stand. Yet he managed to hold them together while he moved across the Colorado and on to the Brazos, then still farther to the Buffalo Bayou which flowed into the San Jacinto River.

Houston hustled his army into a grove of live oaks which fringed the bayou, placing the two cannon, which the men called the "Twin Sisters," so that they commanded the grassy plains over which Santa Anna must come if he attacked.

Deaf Smith came in to report that the Mexicans were massed across the bayou. They had been reinforced by Cos, which raised Santa Anna's number to fourteen hundred against eight hundred Texans.

In the middle of the afternoon Houston formed his volunteers to attack.

"Victory is certain," he said. "Trust in God and fear not." Then he raised his right hand aloft. His eyes blazed as he cried, "Remember the Alamo!"

From the ranks came the resounding echo, "Remember the Alamo!"

The Twin Sisters boomed. Their battle fervor aroused by that cry, "Remember the Alamo," the Texans swept forward with such force that Santa Anna's army turned and fled in terror. The Mexicans were caught completely off guard. The surprise had been complete.

When the Texans ran out of ammunition they pulled out their knives. And so, although James Bowie was not there, the knives which bore his name finally slashed the fetters of despotism which bound Texas. The battle of San Jacinto freed her forever from Mexican tyranny.

CHRONOLOGY

JAMES BOWIE: 1796-1836

1796: Born in Tennessee. Parents moved from Georgia few years before he was born.

1802: Moved to Spanish province of Louisiana, in what is now Catahoula Parish, afterward moving south to vicinity of Opelousas, a region of small prairies, great swamps and vast forests. Land extremely rich. Bowie plantation prospered. James Bowie's boyhood unusual.

1803: Louisiana is purchased by the United States.

1814: James Bowie and his brothers establish a sawmill on Bayou Boeuf.
Battle of New Orleans.

1817-21: Jean Lafitte, privateer, operates on "Galvez-town" Island.

1818: James and Rezin Bowie deal in slave trade with Lafitte.

1819-21: Dr. James Long, filibusterer, leads an expedition into Texas.

1820: Moses Austin secures permission to colonize three hundred Anglo-American families.

1821: The Austin colony, first Anglo-American settlement in Texas, is founded by Stephen Austin.
Mexico gains freedom from Spain, and Texas becomes a Mexican state.

1824-32: Mexico grants colonization contracts to *emprasarios.* Towns of Victoria and Gonzales, founded.

1828: Estimated Anglo-American population, two thousand and twenty.
James Bowie goes to Texas. Takes steps to become a citizen.

1830:		April 6th. Mexico passes law checking further immigration of Anglo-Americans into Texas.
		James Bowie weds Urselita Veramendi, daughter of the Mexican vice-governor.
1831:		Estimated population, exclusive of Indians, twenty thousand.
1832:		Texans and Mexicans clash at Anáhuac and Velasco.
		Convention at San Felipe petitions for political separation of Texas from Coahuila.
1834:		Stephen Austin imprisoned in Mexico.
		After death of his wife and children, Bowie becomes involved in Texas Revolution.
1835:	June 30.	Mexican troops driven from Anáhuac.
	Oct. 2.	Settlers win battle of Gonzales, first battle of Texas revolution.
	Oct. 9.	Texans capture Goliad.
	Oct. 12.	Volunteer Texas army, called the People's Army, under Stephen Austin marches on San Antonio de Bexar, Mexican stronghold.
	Oct. 28.	Battle of Concepción, led by James Bowie aided by James Fannin, is won by Texans.
	Nov. 3.	Provisional government drafted under Governor Henry Smith. Sam Houston made commander in chief of the Armies.
	Dec. 5.	Concluding siege of San Antonio led by Ben Milam.
	Dec. 9.	San Antonio is captured.
	Dec. 10.	Cos, the Mexican general, surrenders.
	Dec. 14.	General Cos and his army depart from Texas, leaving it freed of Mexican soldiers.
1836:	Feb. 15.	Bowie decides to defend the Alamo in order to allow time for Texas to strengthen her defenses.
		General Santa Anna and Mexican army arrive in San Antonio to lay siege to the Alamo.
	Mar. 2.	Declaration of Independence issued at Washington on the Brazos.

Mar. 6. The Alamo falls; every defender dies.

Mar. 13. General Sam Houston, commanding Texas army begins eastward retreat. Gonzales is burned.

Mar. 17. Texas Constitution is adopted at Washington on the Brazos.

Mar. 20. Battle of Coleto ends in surrender of Col. James Fannin and his command.

Mar. 27. Fannin and his men are massacred at Goliad.

April 21. The People's Army, under General Sam Houston, defeats Santa Anna and his army at San Jacinto, thus winning the Texas Revolution and ending Latin domination.

BIBLIOGRAPHY

Primary Sources.

Altsheler, Joseph P. *The Texan Scouts.* N.Y. Appleton, 1937.

Altsheler, Joseph P. *The Texas Star.* N.Y. Appleton, 1920.

Arrington, Alfred M. *Duels & Desperadoes of the Southwest.* No date.

Barr, Amelia E. *Remember the Alamo.* N.Y. Dodd, Mead, 1888.

Barrett, Monte. *Tempered Blade,* Bobbs-Merrill Co., Indianapolis, 1946.

Baker, Eugene Campbell. "Austin Papers." American Historical Assn. Vol. II, 1928.

Boatright, Mody C. & Day, Donald, Eds., "From Hell to Breakfast," Texas Folklore Society, Austin & Univ. Press in Dallas, XIX, 1944.

Bowie, Walter Worthington. *The Bowies and Their Kindred.* Cromwell Press, Washington, 1889.

Butterfield, Jack C. *The Men of the Alamo, Goliad and San Jacinto.* San Antonio. The Naylor Co., 1936.

DeShields, James T. *Tall Men With Long Rifles.* San Antonio. The Naylor Co., 1936.

Dobie, J. Frank. *Coronado's Children,* Grosset & Dunlap, N.Y. 1931.

Dobie, J. Frank. Ed. *In the Shadow of History,* University of Texas, Austin, 1939.

Douglas, C. L. *James Bowie: the Life of a Bravo,* Banks, Upshaw, Dallas, 1944.

Driggs, Howard R., with Sarah S. King. *The Rise of the Lone Star.* N.Y. Frederick A. Stokes Co., 1936.

Driscoll, Clara. *In the Shadow of the Alamo.* N.Y. Putnam Co., 1906.

Duvall, John C. *The Adventures of Bigfoot Wallace,* Dallas, Tardy Co., 1936.

Elfer, Maurice. *Madam Candelaria, Unsung Heroine of the Alamo.* Houston, Rein Co., 1933.

Ellis, Edward S. *The Life of Col. David Crockett,* Henry T. Coates & Co., Phil., 1884. With a sketch of Rezin P. & Col. James Bowie.

Garst, Shannon. *Big Foot Wallace of the Texas Rangers.* N.Y. Julian Messner, Inc., 1951.

Hunter, J. Marvin. *The Trail Drivers of Texas.* Nashville, Tenn. Cokesbury Press, 1925.

Hunter, Therisa M. *Romantic Interludes From the Lives of Texas Heroes.* San Antonio. The Naylor Co., 1936.

James, Marquis. *The Raven, Sam Houston,* Bobbs-Merrill, Indianapolis, 1929.

James, Marquis. *They Had Their Hour.* N.Y. Blue Ribbon Books, 1934.

Linn, John J. *Reminiscences of Fifty Years in Texas.* N.Y. D. & J. Sadlier & Co., 1883.

Lyle, Eugene P. *The Lone Star.* N.Y. Doubleday, Page & Co., 1907.

Monroe, Kirk. *With Crockett & Bowie.* N.Y. Scribner, 1919.

Myers, John. *The Alamo.* E. P. Dutton, N.Y., 1948.

Sabin, Edwin L. *Wild Men of the Wild West,* N.Y. Crowell, 1929.

Sabin, Edwin L. *With Sam Houston in Texas.* Phila. Lipincott, 1916.

Sowell, Andrew Jackson. *Rangers & Pioneers of Texas.* San Antonio. Shepard Bros. & Co., 1884.

Stratemeyer, Edward. *For the Liberty of Texas.* Boston, Lothrop, Lee & Shepherd Co., 1930.

Sutherland, Dr. John. *The Fall of the Alamo.* San Antonio. Naylor, 1936.

Thorpe, Raymond W. *Bowie Knife,* Univ. of New Mexico Press, 1948.

Wellman, Paul I. *The Iron Mistress.* Doubleday, Garden City, N.Y., 1951.

Magazines.

Bowie, John J. "Early Life in the Southwest—the Bowies," *DeBow's Review.* Vol. XIII, Oct. 1852.

Dobie, J. Frank, "Bowie & the Bowie Knife," *Southwest Review* Vol. XVI.

Frost, Meigs. "Bowie & His Big Knife," *Adventure*, June 15, 1935

Lincoln, Robert P. "The Bowie Knife," *Field & Stream.* Dec 1930.

McCullough-Williams, Martha. "A Man and His Knife," *Harper's Magazine*, July, 1898.

Newspapers.

Arkansas Gazette, Little Rock, Nov. 20, 1919.

Dallas Morning News, Jan. 12, 1930.
Oct. 13, 1925.

Galveston Daily News, Mar. 6, 1880.
Mar. 31, 1890.
Mar. 21, 1920.

New Orleans Times-Picayune, Apr. 26, 1925.

San Antonio Evening News, Feb. 27, 1929.

Texas Sentinel, Austin, Feb. 11, 1841.

Texas Telegraph & Register, Houston, Jan. 21, 1841
June 20, 1850

Reference Works.

Dictionary of American Biography, N.Y. 1929.

Encyclopedia Americana, N.Y. 1932.

Manuscripts.

"Fontaine Papers." Univ. of Texas Archives.

Ford, John S. "Memoirs." Univ. of Texas Archives.

Theses.

Williams, Amelia. *A Critical Study of the Siege of the Alamo*, 1931, The Univ. of Texas Library.

Rohrbough, Edward, Jr. *James Bowie and the Bowie Knife in Fact and Fiction*, 1938, The University of Texas Library.

Secondary Sources.

Crockett, David. *Autobiography of David Crockett,* N.Y. Scribners, 1923.

Seitz, Don C. *Famous American Duels,* N.Y. Crowell, 1929.

Quarterly of the Louisiana Historical Society, Vol. XV. Oct. 1932, pp. 638-645.

INDEX